About Teaching Companion

The 4MAT® Implementation Workbook

by Bernice McCarthy and Dennis McCarthy

Illustrated by Margaret Gray Hudson

Published by About Learning, Incorporated

About Learning, Incorporated
Wauconda, IL
May, 2003

Art direction, book and cover design
by Mary Fran Zidron.
Set in Cheltenham and Charlotte Sans type.
Printed by Mid-American Printing Systems, Inc.,
Chicago, IL.
ISBN: 1-929040-03-2

*4MAT and 4MATION are registered trademarks
of About Learning, Inc.*

The 4MAT Implementation Workbook

The purpose of this workbook is to assist practitioners in the implementation of 4MAT.

4MAT is a huge paradigm shift from the notion that...

> *"Students learn based on their ability, and if they take the opportunity and work hard."*

To the commitment that...

> *"We will take responsibility for all students and provide the resources and help they need to achieve exceptional knowledge and skills."*

This shift implies that all kids can learn. An amazing idea!

May this workbook help that to be so.

–Bernice McCarthy

Table of Contents

The About Teaching Companion

The exercises that follow are designed to help 4MAT teachers further their adaptation of 4MAT and integrate 4MAT principles into their everyday instruction.

Chapters One through Eight include in-depth exploration of essential skills for working at exemplary levels with 4MAT including:

Enhancing lessons using right-mode strategies.

Understanding how concept-based teaching is the *only* way you can engage learners at the outset of a lesson.

Understanding each of the quadrants of 4MAT, represented by the wheel that addresses the **Why**, **What**, **How** and **If** in turn.

Scaling criteria for evaluating instruction in terms of the 4MAT framework.

We use sample units throughout to illustrate specifics and as working documents for possible expansion and enhancement.

In **Chapter Nine**, we present a template for aligning state and district standards with curriculum, illustrated by a sample two-semester course developed in a project with Indiana standards and curriculum.

Chapter Ten offers the latest research on 4MAT implementation for review and questioning, and includes an historical overview of major 4MAT theorists.

Use this workbook as a coaching tool.

Work in the sections that you need to revisit. If assessment is of most concern to you, go to that section. If conceptualizing content still is difficult, go there.

You will find it helpful to work with a small group of fellow teachers to maximize the benefits of the practice exercises created here.

Bonita Springs, Florida
Spring, 2003.

Section One

Chapters 1-8

Deeper into 4MAT Instruction

Chapter One

The Brain
Preparing Your Palette

Consciousness begins with a feeling.
—Domasio

The Brain
Preparing Your Palette

We begin this workbook with a look at enhancing instruction by understanding right and left mode strategies. The combination of these strategies will affect how your learners both take in and express learning. Think of these strategies as preparing to paint a picture by adding colors onto your palette. As we delve more deeply into the process of looking at units around a 4MAT framework, you will pull and mix the colors of your palette.

Humans move from **perception** to **focus** to **emotion** to **images** to **concepts and symbols** to **use** to **creative reasoning** to **insight and intuition** to **vision and possibility**—a constant interplay between right- and left-mode processing.

This is how the brain works,
and that is how the cycle flows.

If this is true, the top half of the cycle takes on new meaning.

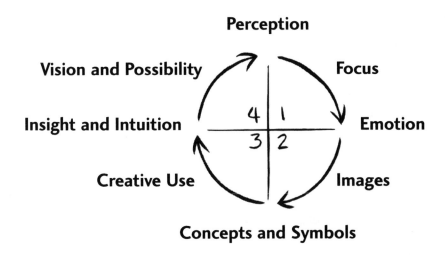

There are higher modes of development beyond rationality.

True/False:
test your current brain knowledge

	True	False

1. Brain and body run on electricity.

2. In the first year of a baby's life the brain
   quadruples in size.

3. A gene wakes up when it learns.

4. Language lights up the right hemisphere.

5. Most brain cells survive through a lifetime.

6. Making connections is what brain cells live for.

7. Depressed parents reduce an infant's ability to
   experience joy.

8. It is now held that the left hemisphere mediates
   intrinsic alertness.

9. The notion that the mind and the body are separate
   is down the drain.

10. The right hemisphere is dominant in human
    infants for the first three years.

11. Loneliness reduces immune response.

12. Memory is like a Xerox.

13. The mind constructs a world.

14. The human brain thinks in two distinctive ways:
    rational and connective.

15. Our mental models determine what we see, all are
    flawed in some way.

Some Brain Comments

Nature or nurture, the tyranny of the single cause, has been thrown into the dustbin with history's other useless ideas…To scientists who use brain-imaging devices to watch the brain as it remembers, imagines, and desires, it is awe inspiring. But the large question remains: how can this ebb and flow of blood, this intricate web of connections, become the experience of our feelings, the content of our thoughts?

It is precisely this question that will occupy us for the next fifty years…

The neurologist Alvaro Pascual-Leone has shown that the brains of professional musicians undergo functional and structural changes as they train, changes that can be documented by neuroimaging techniques…

This three-pound organ, packed with billions of neurons rivaling in their numbers the stars in our galaxy and equipped with up to two hundred thousand synaptic connections to other neurons, is the most complex structure in the universe.

—Nancy Etcoff, Harvard Faculty of Medicine, 1999

Start with this question.

☆ How can this flow of blood, this web of connections become our feelings, our thoughts?

☆ What is your initial feeling as you read this quote?

☆ Do you agree with this statement regarding the solid connection between the mind and the body? What does this mean for teaching? How does this idea that "things" must connect relate to teaching?

More Comments from Researchers

Note the continuing emphasis on connections to past experience, the Quadrant One focus in 4MAT.

Once the brain is engaged and attentive, chemical and electrical charges seek connections to related information along neural circuits. Once the connection has been made to past information, the new neural highway is created.
—Pamela Nevills, 2003

Our experience of reality is constructed by the activity patterns of neuronal groups within the brain. The patterns of communication within early relationships directly shape the development of the mind.
–Daniel Siegel, 1999

During the past three decades, we've learned more about the brain than in all of recorded history…this knowledge is an essential element on which we base our educational decisions.
The person doing the work is the one growing the dendrites.
—Pat Wolfe, 2001

Your brain is unique,
is capable of making an unlimited number of synaptic connections
can learn seven facts per second, every second, for the rest of your life
and still have plenty of room left over to learn more,
will improve with age if you use it properly.
—Michael Gelb, 1998

We need to design instruction to match how the brain learns—
Instruction that allows students to connect new learning to past experiences increases the power of neural connections, and results in increased memory.
—Bernice McCarthy

The BRAIN—is wider than the sky—.
—Emily Dickinson

☆ **Write your own personal definition of brain here.**

Now Revisit the Right- and Left-mode Idea

A poem begins
as a lump in the throat,
a sense of wrong,
a homesickness,
a love sickness.
It is never a thought to begin with.
—Robert Frost

We should take care
not to make the intellect our god;
it has, of course,
powerful muscles,
but no personality.
It cannot lead;
it can only serve.
—Albert Einstein

The plight of mankind is all the fault of the human mind being made in two lobes, only one of which does any thinking, so we are all right-handed or left-handed; whereas, if we were properly constructed, we should use our right and left hands with equal force and skill according to circumstances. As it is, those who can win a war well can rarely make a good peace, and those who could make a good peace never win.
—Winston Churchill

☆ What are these three men saying? Do you agree? If they are correct, what are the ramifications for decision-making, for exceptional thinking?

Understanding can be symbolized and to some extent conveyed through words, but understanding itself requires language no more than a bird requires a cage. Understanding comes only through experience, and for experience, there has never been—and never will be—a substitute.
—Ken Carey

☆ What is Carey talking about? How can you understand without words? Come up with one example. Share it with your peers.

☆ **Review this list of synonyms for "Knowing". Circle those you consider "right mode".**

apprehension

cognizance

comprehension

conception

discrimination

enlightenment

experience

expertise

identification

illumination

insight

instinct

intimacy

intuition

meeting

penetration

rationality

realization

recognition

remembrance

scholarship

sensing

understanding

learning

Recently 600 students, who were aware of The 4MAT Cycle and who were learning in 4MAT classrooms, were asked to rate their favorite steps. They consistently chose the right mode **Connect**, **Image**, **Extend**, **Perform** steps over the left mode **Attend**, **Inform**, **Practice**, **Refine** steps.

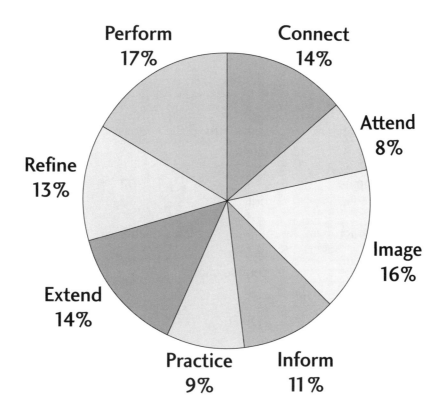

Why do you suppose this is? Because they're more "fun"? Because these teaching methods are not prevalent in traditional school settings? Do you believe students learn more during left mode "telling" steps or during right mode "doing" steps? Why?

Using right mode strategies in the classroom needn't be difficult. Good teachers do it all the time. It can be something as simple as wearing period clothing, playing Copland in the background while rendering a dramatic reading of the Gettysburg address.

In the current climate of knowledge and skills and accountability, more than ever your students need you to be creative.

Left Mode Words

☆ Sometimes, determining whether an activity is right mode or left can be as simple as looking at the key words. Here is a partial list of words that are considered left mode. Circle the ones that are most prevalent in your teaching.

observe   read   reason   order   come to closure

discuss   view   identify   select   refocus

diverge   research   break into parts   flowchart   produce

develop coherence   compare   drill   write an essay   take a position

                 contrast   edit

conceptualize   uncover contradictions   conclude

                 plan   revise

define

                 theorize   collect   refine   form new questions

classify

                 outline   inquire   produce evidence

discriminate

                                predict

                 test   verify

acquire knowledge   record

                 verify   summarize

tell   hypothesize

                 analyze   assess

listen   measure

                 write analytically   evaluate

sit still   manage

Now the Right Mode Words

☆ Circle the ones that you use most.

reflect

relate

journal

brainstorm

visualize

imagine

draw

create a mindmap

associate

simulate

role-play

connect

express

interact

write creatively or poetically

pattern

contrast

feel tone

feel timbre

feel nuance

represent

illustrate

cluster

tinker

hunch

relate to real world

demonstrate

synthesize

exhibit

publish

author

merge to a higher form

integrate

create

experiment

A Bushel Basket of Right Mode Activities

This left-right division of mind is profound and the difference runs deep. The right hemisphere is greatly involved in discovering the gist of passages. Yet we remain anchored in instruction that is designed for:

uniformity,

control of inputs and behavior,

confirmation of the teacher's/instructor's knowledge,

repetition of activities and information,

linearity, in thinking and in sequencing.

This is incompatible with how the brain works!

On the next pages, we invite you to examine some strategies that favor the right mode. These strategies are based on the material found in the text *About Teaching: 4MAT in the Classroom.*

Mindmapping in Action

These are stream of consciousness drawings where one idea presents another, and another. Ideas are drawn as they seem to relate to each other, using various shapes and directions. Both vertical operations are used, as in sets and subsets, as well as horizontal lines to indicate relationships.

Asking your students to create mindmaps is a brain- and memory-compatible strategy that greatly increases their understanding of the big picture. It also helps teachers to have a sense of the important ideas that surround an idea. Use them to list all that is involved with a unit and as a double-check against standards (directly related and from other subject areas).

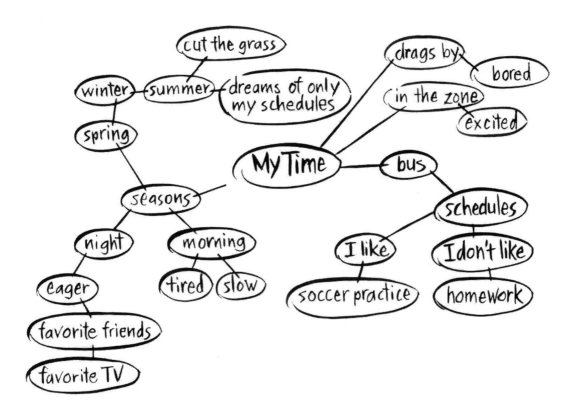

A student sample on "My Time"

Try it! We have created some sample mindmaps. Fill in some of the blanks, then add your own branches. Try creating interactive mindmaps on the board. Try creating mindmaps that "grow" over the course of a unit. If you have access to the *Inspiration*® software, use it in front of the classroom for brainstorming sessions.

☆ 1. Unit based

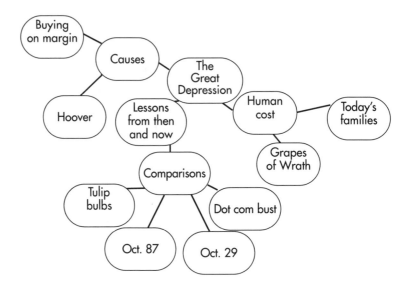

☆ 2. Curriculum-Based

Try sharing **ALL** the connections with students. You'll be surprised at how much of the big picture they can see. We've left some balloons empty for you to fill in on your own. Feel free to add spokes.

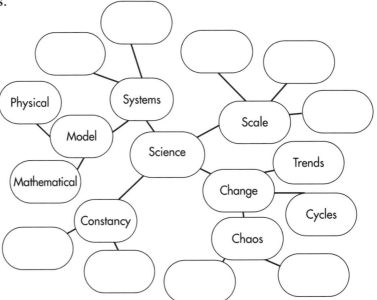

Chapter One: The Brain–Preparing Your Palette

☆ 3. Concept-Based

(see more on concepts and concept-based curriculum in the *Concepts and Standards* sections of this workbook)

After you have brainstormed some of the ideas for this concept-based mindmap, consider it against your standards requirements. Can you relate particular standards to these ideas?

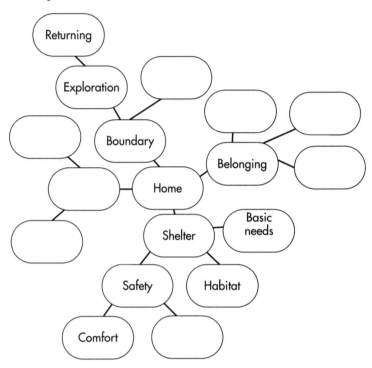

Nonverbal Representations in Action

Use symbols, shapes, literal representations and nonliteral representations (squiggles, vortex type delineations, etc.) to illustrate understanding.

RAGE

HAPPINESS

SERENITY

HOPELESSNESS

☆ Example: Use a nonverbal series of just lines, no literal pictures, to capture what you think is the essence of the short story, *A Separate Piece.*

☆ Use this mini-worksheet to brainstorm your ideas for using nonverbal representation in the classroom. While there is no specific formula for these ideas, they all share common elements; they are *non* reading and writing expressions of ideas and understandings.

examples　　　　Now you try. Brainstorm nonverbal representation examples for:

Science

| Students create a bird of their own design using torn up paper. What features are important? |
| Students create a visual or 3-dimensional metaphor of refraction |

Growth	Cells	Equilibrium	Interconnected-ness of Living Things	Adaptation

Math

| Students record and draw patterns found in nature |
| In groups, students demonstrate imbalance kinesthetically, artistically and dramatically |

Place Value	Fractions	Functions	Sets	Estimation

Social Studies

| Students draw a picture of what the world would look like if there were no rules |
| Students create a media collage depicting gender stereotypes |

Scarcity	Political Systems	Supply and Demand	Trade among Nations	Impact of Technology

Language

| Students create a visual analog portraying the feeling of being walled out or walled in |
| Students create an interpretive symbol of a poem; then capture the essence with a word or short phrase |

Haiku	Sentence Structure	Short Story	Persuasion	Public Speaking

Created with Inspiration®.

Brainstorm other ideas with peers and be sure to include art and music.

☆ **Now try it with things you are teaching.**

Patterning

Seeing patterns in ideas, texts, and all manner of visuals, looking at the whole to discern similarities and repetitions. Encourage your students to see the discrepancies in patterns as well.

Example: Create a record of how you spend your time, when you get home from school until you go to bed, for five school nights. Describe any pattern you see, comment on how happy you are with what you see, and suggest possible options for what you might want to change.

Using Imagery

Create pictures of concepts, relationships, and connections. Put thoughts into three-dimensional space to better understand associations, links, and overall coherence. Figurative language provides intensity as well as clarification, helps to illuminate an idea, to forge comparisons.

Example: Depict the essay you wrote on justice, the police and teenagers with images that explain your thinking and your feelings on the subject. You may use magazine images or original ones. Be sure your feelings are clear to the observer of your work.

Raising Sensory Awareness

Using techniques that call on auditory, visual, kinesthetic, tactile and olfactory (smell) senses as a key to more enriched understanding and to add perspective from different angles.

Example: Find music that sounds like joy, or melancholy, or triumph. Explain what made it so. Or dance the meaning of startling change. Or tell me what anger smells like. Or create a texture that feels like competition.

Poetic Language

All the uses of poetic language: metrics (the way a line breathes), pattern and sound merging, balance and design, rhyme and energy, all these can be used to create images that tell so much more than mere literal text. Poetic language can be used in many more content areas than one would think. It is a truly fine match to some areas of mathematics, for instance. It is an excellent technique for aiding understanding, especially with students who seem to naturally gravitate to that type of language.

Example: Describe the Doppler effect with only rhyming nouns, no verbs. Write a haiku about photosynthesis.

Analogies

These can be drawings or words or images that represent comparisons based on similarities.

Each of us has an outer and an inner mental life—the former uses ordinary language, but the latter cannot be expressed in words because of its complexity. So the goal is to use visual rather than verbal language to make these complex things, the human interactive things, visible, to give them form.

Art can convey thought in such a way as to make it directly perceptible.

—Max Bill in *The Mathematical Approach to Art*

Example: Analogies can help students capture the essence of things. For example, have students draw an analogy for the core idea of the short story you just read.

The Use of Paradox

A statement exhibiting inexplicable or contradictory aspects, patterning balance and tensions in both verbal and nonverbal compositions.

Example: Ask students, "What if the exact opposite is true, what would that be like?" Find ways to have your students illustrate the balance and the lack of balance that often exist together in compositions of all kinds—an invitation to take a deeper look. Examine the profound truth concerning balance in the universe. Use the behavior of subatomic systems to illustrate.

Three-dimensional Tasks

All manner of building assignments, but not limited to only concrete tasks. Ask your students to create their answers in three dimensions to the essential questions you pose in your major units. Have them build forms to illustrate their ideas and to show meanings.

Example: Create a three-dimensional version of a core belief in a certain culture. This assignment would lead your students to examine the artifacts of that culture more closely.

Clustering Disparate Things or Ideas into New Groupings or Formations

This is the metaphor idea again. Putting multiple, seemingly "dis-alike" things together in new ways is a challenge to the creative mode, and a fine way to achieve new insights.

Example: How is a corporation like a garden? like a train station? like plaster?

Dramatics and Movement

All form of role-playing and creative dramatics engage the senses, visual, auditory, kinesthetic, etc. The creation of scripts involves interpersonal understandings. Have them build storylines that illustrate building tensions among individuals, and so on. This technique has so many positives, including great fun. Why teachers do not use it more is a real puzzle to me.

Example: Create a role-play wherein one of you is the father, and one the son who just received a very poor report card. And it is the first half of the son's senior year. (I actually did this one with a class of high school seniors, and the results were not only profound, but also hilarious. Much good came out of that exchange that day.)

Ask your student to demonstrate understandings with body motion, especially without words. This reveals the underlying meanings of ideas. I remember a group of high school seniors who "performed" the process of photosynthesis in complete silence. Ask them today all these years later what they remember about that science class and they will say, "We remember photosynthesis."

☆ Use this mini-worksheet to brainstorm the possible uses of dramatics and movement in the regular classroom. Don't forget to invite the drama teacher!

4MAT in Action!

Examples of Dramatics

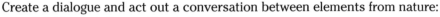

Create a dialogue and act out a conversation between key historical figures (who may or may not have been contemporaries). Be sure to list what must be discussed but also leave room for student topics of conversation.

Create a dialogue and act out a conversation between elements from nature:
a light beam talking with a prism,
an atom about to be split (on a firing line),
a friendship between oxygen and hydrogen, and carbon dioxide.

Dramatically represent concepts in math:
place value concept presented by human numbers,
students in different-colored shirts acting out set operations,
balance in Algebra with a tug-of-war or teeter-totter demonstration with human X's and Y's.

Ask students to present improvisational skits that bring together disparate elements:
the framers of the Constitution in a negotiation session with the King of England, laying out their demands; the king's reactions,
Albert Einstein meets Minnesota Fats in a championship pool game,
Galileo, Stephen Hawking and Christopher Columbus walking the beach on a starry night.

Present new ideas in History and Literature with period music, clothing and speech.

Examples of Movement

Use movement to silently portray...

the process of cell division	sine waves
friction	decay
exponential growth	balance
conflict	an important discovery
natural selection	fractions
equations	enzymes
slavery	

☆ List other concepts that might work well with Dramatics and Movement

_____   _____

_____   _____

_____   _____

Scanning

Scanning is a vital skill students need to master if they are to become adults who understand "the big picture" as well as the details.

Our left brains have become stiff with technique, far from the scanning eye.

–Jerome Bruner, 1962, 1979

Teach them to skim certain texts for the main idea, to scan a complicated work of art for just a few moments and then tell each other what they saw. Have them find patterns in the way their fellow students mingle and talk and act on a minimally supervised playground.

Tinkering—All Kinds

Encourage your students to tinker. Give them permission to find things out for themselves. Set up experiments with many different possible and equally good results and conclusions. Their right brains will thank you.

Using Color and Tone to Illustrate, to Compare, to Enrich

Use color to describe a person, a poem, a story, an idea.

> Example: If you had to choose a color to describe Harry Potter, what might it be? Would Hermione be a different color?

Parallel Processing

Juxtaposing ideas (side by side) to better understand both.

> Example: Put the idea of chaos side by side with the idea of order. Can you find order in chaos and chaos in order? How? Give examples.

Stream of Consciousness: Writing, Thinking, Journaling

Encourage this most subjective action as worthwhile and insightful. Let your students know that they know more than they know. Teach them to trust their perceptions and emotions without worrying about whether something is said well or perfectly. The refinements come later, the insights are key here.

The key here is that schools very rarely ask students to express what is deep in their hearts, to express themselves using their developing skills about something that it truly important to them. When you ask for this, you will see how they really write. And you will not find this on even the most innovative standardized test.

Geometry

The measurements and relationships of points, lines, angles, surfaces, and solids. The spatial dimension of geometry puts it in a class by itself, so different from the left-mode processing of algebra. Notice the students who seem to take to Geometry naturally. Some will tell you it is absolutely fascinating to them. There may be two entirely different ways to approach Math, the logical algebraic way and the visual-spatial way. Use the visual spatial skills of Geometry to examine illustrations of relationships in other content areas. Have your students demonstrate the essence of one of their essays visually. They can use circles within circles, arrows connecting parts, etc. An interesting fact that in spite of the troubles in school experienced by Einstein, Edison, and DaVinci, they all shared a common trait, a natural interest and ability in geometry.

Most Math Conceptualizing

The mathematical thinker is one who above all is a student of puzzle forms. There are right- and left-mode aspects in the teaching of Math. Set up discovery, bring forth the courage in your students to trust their own intuition (which precedes proof). Teach students to translate intuitive ideas into mathematical statements that can be tested. Math presents the most exciting possibilities for whole brain strategies, and yet sadly, most math is taught in only left-mode ways.

It is the intuitive mode that yields hypotheses quickly, interesting combinations of ideas before their worth is known. The intuitive insight is exactly what the techniques of analysis and proof are designed to test and check. It is founded on a kind of combinatorial playfulness… depending in great measure on the confidence one has in the process rather than on the right answers.

–Jerome Bruner, 1962, 1979

Consider the math of music, of poetry, of great writing.

Finding Similarities Across Diverse Domains

If the teacher conceptualizes the issues well, the big ideas will present engaging combinations that students will discover across disciplines.

> Example: If the concept is "change," have students in your Social Studies class illustrate the concept from three different disciplines: science, human development theory and their own community life.

Using Music to Accompany, Compare, Augment or even Explain

Music is seldom used well, even by music teachers. Think of explaining a short story with a musical composition that illustrates the same mood, issues, or emotion. The word music comes from a Latin root meaning "art of the muses".

It is generally agreed that Mozart used G minor to express melancholy. The Greeks linked certain musical modes to particular emotions.

–Anthony Storr, 1992

There is music in so many things. Feelings, nuance, self expression, the way we converse. Music can be used to convey meaning in a way that nothing else can. It is "texture in the air".

Music is proof of the inexpressible. For those who don't yet possess the gifts of the poet, music can convey the feelings that are impossible to articulate with words.

Example: Ask students to liken punctuation to musical rests, symbols, dynamics, directions, writing the same "sentence" with words, then with music, then perhaps with movement.

Have your students take a main emotion from a piece of literature and match it to a piece of music.

Musical training is a more potent instrument than any other, because rhythm and harmony find their way into the inward places of the soul, resulting in gracefulness.

–Anthony Storr, 1992

Example: Use music to set tones in your classrooms. What kind of music would you use to introduce binomials in algebra, what kind to introduce James Joyce's *The Dubliners* in Senior Lit? How can you incorporate popular music (the music your students listen to) into your classroom?

☆ Use this mini-worksheet to brainstorm the possible uses of music in the regular classroom. Don't forget to invite a music teacher or musician!

Examples in Social Studies and Literature	Your examples
What music was important at this time in history? Is there any particular style of music that defined this era? Are there parallels between the characteristics of the music of the time and the characteristics of the visual art or literature? For example, Impressionistic music and Impressionistic art share softness, lack of linearity, etc.	

Examples in Science and Math	Your examples
Is there music that characterizes this concept? Try Stravinsky for Chaos, try a Bach fugue for balance.	

Examples in any subject	Your examples
Can music be used to introduce a new idea dramatically? Is there a musical metaphor for this thing? For example, punctuation with musical notation, rhythm with mathematical patterns, the movement of light with the movement of sound, musical expression and dynamics with literary expression.	

Demonstrations

The act of presenting information in ways that have to be used, rather than just explained, calls upon a plethora of expertise. Successful demonstrations require students to produce a number of things. They need good visuals, or working models. They need to interact with their audience, and possess a real grasp of the material they are presenting. Create specific rubrics (lists of criteria) for exemplary demonstrations.

There are multiple advantages to demonstrations.

> They allow you to delve deeper into a subject (a *must* in the current climate of "coverage first").

> They allow you to create individual or group "student experts".

> They force students to get to know the content at a deeper level.

> They allow for different representations of understanding, capitalizing on learner diversity.

This well-rounded approach to assessment raises the odds that learners will "get it" and retain it.

Technology plays an important role in these demonstrations. Many schools have demonstration tools that rival what is available in corporate boardrooms. You can use these tools to allow learners to express understanding in multiple ways.

☆ Try the mini-worksheet on the following page to help you start thinking about creative demonstrations in the classroom. Be sure to think in terms of authoring tools and multiple media.

Chapter One: The Brain–Preparing Your Palette

Example in Language	Your examples
Create a slideshow that combines still images, music, and dramatic reading to portray the feeling of a poet's work.	for Sentence Structure: for _____: (your content choice)

Example in Science	Your examples
Create a **PowerPoint**® presentation that compares and contrasts how different forms and structures reflect different functions (e.g., similarities and differences among animals that fly, walk or swim). Present and narrate.	for Photosynthesis: for _____: (your content choice)

Example in Social Studies	Your examples
Create a web site that examines two differing perspectives on the separation of church and state with links to articles, images, and guided presentation.	for Ancient People: for _____: (your content choice)

Example in Math	Your examples
Use **iMovie**® to present a top-ten list of Algebra in the world.	for Set Operations: for _____: (your content choice)

Hunching

Encourage your students to hunch. Set up situations where hunching is valued, and help them analyze the steps they follow in order to confirm or rule out their hunches. An experiment in science, or an idea about why someone acted the way they did, followed by an interview to confirm or rule out, or a search for the root cause of a complicated problem.

This is problem-solution-based teaching. It taps directly into the creative imaginations of learners and intrigues them when solutions "become informed". It also allows teachers to steer learners in a sudden new direction, examining different perspectives.

☆ Try the sample worksheet to get yourself started with how to add hunching to your classroom.

Examples in Literature	Your example
The Problem: Bigotry and Uninformed Perceptions **Supporting Content:** *To Kill a Mockingbird* **Hunch This:** What changes would be made in this school to make it so everyone were treated as they should be treated. **The Problem:** Scarcity **Supporting Content:** *Grapes of Wrath* **Hunch This:** What would you do if you had to suddenly raise your family on one tenth of your present income?	**The Problem:** **Supporting Content:** **Hunch This:**

Example in Social Studies	Your example
The Problem: Social Chaos **Supporting Content:** Rules in society **Hunch This:** What would this school look like if there were *no* rules? Would even the students want just a few rules? Which rules would they add first?	**The Problem:** **Supporting Content:** **Hunch This:**

Example in English/Language Arts	Your example
The Problem: Communicating emotion in written form	**The Problem:**
Supporting Content: Poetry	
Hunch This: What process do you suppose poets go through as they attempt to "find the right words" to portray deep feelings and emotions?	**Supporting Content:** **Hunch This:**

Examples in Math	Your example
The Problem: Unknowns	**The Problem:**
Supporting Content: Variables	
Hunch This: How might you gauge the opinions of 1000 people on 20 different questions? Would you use a computer? What would the computer have to do?	**Supporting Content:**
The Problem: Hitting a Target	**Hunch This:**
Supporting Content: Cartesian Coordinate System	
Hunch This: Try hitting a target with a makeshift cannon. How might you succeed 100% of the time? Can you develop a system that makes it possible for anyone to hit the target using any cannon?	

Example in Science	Your example
The Problem: Your species is becoming extinct	**The Problem:**
Supporting Content: Adaptation	
Hunch This: What do you hunch needs to be present in the environment for a species to survive? Why do you suppose some species are able to succeed in the seemingly hostile environment of encroaching development while others die?	**Supporting Content:** **Hunch This:**

Body Language

All manner of body language skills engage the right mode. Your students will love it! Ask them in what situations they really need to understand body language and then have them simulate such situations for each other. The result is very insightful and goes much deeper into inter- and intra-personal intelligence issues.

Reflective Dialogues in which Language is Used to Focus on the Mental States of Others

What was the main character feeling during this scene? If you were in that situation, what would you be feeling? Use this technique not only to understand literature, but also to create original dramatic presentations.

Alice laughed. "There's no use trying," she said.

"One cannot believe impossible things."

"I daresay you haven't had much practice," said the Queen.

"When I was your age, I always did it for half an hour a day. Why, sometimes I've believed in as many as six impossible things before breakfast!"

—Lewis Carroll

Polysemantic Images of the World

Ask your students to create many meanings for one word. For example, words like **gist**, **wonder**, **sweet**, **snow**, **fence**, **major**. This is a fine strategy to get students to open themselves to many possible answers, to see more than single meanings from ideas and words. Also use combinations of all those techniques listed here adding many of your own.

Autobiographical Memories with Emotional Meaning

Have your students focus on memorable events in their lives, even perhaps those that were turning points. The understandings from these insights may be used in a variety of ways, in original stories and dramatic presentations, juxtaposed beside a hero or heroine in a literature piece, or even examined through the lens of a musical piece. Students come to insightful understandings when they return to events that had great meaning. Ask a group of students to recount such events to each other and have them create a short drama together illustrating a composite of these events. This is a very powerful process. Your students will learn much from each other.

Practice in Translating this Research into Strategies for Whole-Brain Instruction

The following pages explore in greater depth how to use five key strategies that lend themselves to using both right- and left-mode processing in your teaching

1. images, visual representation

2. metaphors, implicit comparisons

3. roundness, working from whole to part

4. patterns, designs, structures or configurations that appear

5. graphic organizers, the use of spatial relationships to illustrate a concept, an event, a story structure

1. Images

In some cases, it seems that the greater the fluency with nonverbal thought, the greater the dysfluency of verbal communication. This tendency might create difficulties for those in universities and other institutions where verbal proficiency is seen as a major indicator of intellectual competence.

—Thomas West, 1991

☆ Comment/reflect on this quote. Do you know people who are gifted visually but not very glib speakers? On the other hand do you know people who are very good verbally, but have real difficulty with nonverbal understanding?

☆ What is the teacher's task with both of these learners, the verbally astute and the visually astute?

☆ If possible discuss this with a colleague or group.

Can you really understand something if you cannot visualize it in your mind? Think of some of the math operations you were taught. Did you see the pictures in your mind, or were they just meaningless equations to solve, with no apparent purpose other than to satisfy your math teacher, and to complete the exercises in the math workbook?

When you saw the picture of standard deviation did it become more clear? Did its meaning make more sense? If you were one of the lucky ones and you had a math teacher who always showed you the pictures, I'll wager you got it. Many others did not.

How is it that when we are able to create the images of things, as well as classify them with words we really understand them conceptually?

What if Eisner and Arnheim are right when they claim:

Unless we can image a process or a concept we cannot understand it?

☆ **Why do you think that is? Why do we really need both?**

The right-mode step of Quadrant Two leading into the left-mode step of Quadrant Two is based on the need to image to understand.

Examine the following lesson. As you do so think about images.

What could be added to enhance the ability of the students to picture the concept, to understand it at a nonverbal level?

Middle School Mathematics

A 4MAT lesson plan

Concept: Symbols in Math—Geometry Symbols

Author: Vera Hayes

This is the third lesson in a three-lesson series on Symbols in Math.

The teacher's first 4MAT wheel was a general overview of symbols focusing on their use in the general lives of the students. The second wheel focused on distance, direction and opposites and the corresponding need for integers/rational numbers and the zero.

This third lesson moves into the symbols and vocabulary of geometry.

Quadrant One, Right Mode

Students create a design from a set of geometric shapes they are given. They work in pairs. One creates the design behind a barrier as the other tries to discover exactly what the design is, based on the partner's description of it.

The partners change roles and repeat the task.

Quadrant One, Left Mode

Students list the vocabulary used to describe the designs. The lists are combined into a class list and posted along with a discussion of the importance of correct vocabulary.

Quadrant Two, Right Mode

The pairs of students choose any two letters from the alphabet and describe their similarities and differences. Each pair exchanges their descriptions with another pair and they try to determine which letter is being described.

Quadrant Two, Left Mode

The teacher gives instruction and illustrations about the terms, symbols, and vocabulary used in geometry. Students have reading assignments in text.

Quadrant Three, Left Mode

Students answer questions from the text, complete worksheets and take a quiz.

Quadrant Three, Right Mode

Students choose from the following:

Research the history of geometric symbols.

Find math symbols and organize them into families and make a mobile display with written explanations included.

Create a booklet about symbols and the order of operations as if you were teaching a younger student.

Create a set of cartoons illustrating the order of operations, integers, math symbols or geometry vocabulary. Check the book *Humor in Math* first.

Quadrant Four, Left Mode

Students prepare project plans, students help each other and teacher OKs the project.

Quadrant Four, Right Mode

Students complete their projects and share them with their classmates.

☆ Was the use of images sufficient for the teacher's purpose?

☆ Could more have been done? How?

☆ What did you think of the strategy of organizing math symbols into families?

Possible Improvements to this Lesson in Terms of Images

The Visual Explorer: Educator's Edition

Further explore the use of images in your teaching with the following ten images and teaching ideas taken from The Visual Explorer.

The Visual Explorer is a collection of over 300 high-quality images that help teachers make connections across multiple disciplines, using images as building blocks to achieve higher levels of understanding and dialogue.

A7 Abstracts
Describe the feeling you get from this image and share it with a partner.

A10 Abstracts
Name this image and the emotion it expresses.

C1 Antiquity
Create a story of what happened in the one hour preceding this image.

D1 Celebration
Interview this person: create 5 questions and 5 answers.

D2 Celebration
Find a piece of music to go with this image.

E8 Communication
Describe the type of communication you see.

F5 Courage
Complete the statement, "Courage is…"

G1 Diversity
Based on the image, list 5 things that are probably true about these people.

H4 Earth and Sky
Be this image and talk to the people of the earth.

N3 People in Relationships
Write 10 lines of dialogue between the people in this image.

Chapter One: The Brain–Preparing Your Palette

2. Metaphors

Metaphor definition: one thing used to represent another, not meant literally but to make a comparison.

Using metaphors may be one of the most rewarding right-mode activities, because of the possible payoff. When we create a metaphor, we must understand the core of something in order to contrast it with something else.

Try answering these yourself: How is a tree like a poem? What metaphor will describe best for you the meaning of an algorithm?

Creating metaphors sends you to the essence. What is the heart of the meaning of Huck Finn? The process of photosynthesis?

☆ Examine the use of metaphor in this poem. Spend a few minutes in a small group or with a colleague/coach discussing the richness of the metaphors in terms of describing the coming of spring.

Spring on Honey Lake

Spring to me is when the water moves
The cracking time,
Dark slits widening in the ice.

Humble Honey Lake, small, reedy, a metaphor profound
Lying at my porch's feet,
A testament each day.

It is spring to me when I question things
My growing time,
The nudge to find a new sweet dance
A clearing, a rounder space with barricades aside
Leaving the certain snarled
A journey to myself.

It is to let go that we are here.
To have cracking times.
Dark slits in our ice.

Our grandest task,
the great quest of our lives, is to find that place
where we can be water
where we can be eternal Spring.

–Bernice McCarthy

Some examples of metaphors used in different disciplines from *Teaching Creativity through Metaphor* (Sanders, 1984).

Political Science: democratic monarchy can be like the liberty found inside a bee hive, freedom within defined roles and clear expectations.

Science: osmosis can be explained as a process that resembles a sponge.

Citizenship: tolerance can be likened to the acceptance of an army of different plants in the garden, each having its own season and its own contributions.

Math: square root can be compared to center beams in a four-sided house.

☆ Now take one of your own lessons, add a metaphor technique and teach the lesson with the metaphor added. Note what happens to your students' clarity of understanding. Share what happens with a peer, coach or a group.

☆ How vital are metaphors to help students understand? Help each other come up with more ways to use metaphors.

☆ Here's a great question: **Can you use metaphor effectively in the left mode sections as well?**

☆ Your activity **before** metaphor enhancement:

☆ Your activity **after** metaphor enhancement:

☆ What happened when you tried it?

3. Roundness

How can you help your students think **"round"**?

Round = context, all at once, big picture, other connections.

You need to teach conceptually. You need to go to the essence of what you are teaching and conceptualize it.

Maybe a teacher could...

connect Columbus to exploration

connect hair design to contour

connect magnets to force

connect quadratic equations to balance

connect immigration to the courage to be a stranger

and so on.

Teachers need to get the concept, the deep part, the connection. Concepts lead to more things than just the details. Concepts lead to universal applications.

Master teachers conceptualize. For detailed information on Conceptualizing, refer to Chapter 2 of this workbook.

Examine the following lesson in terms of **"Roundness"**.

A 4MAT lesson plan

Aloha ʻÄina (Love of the Land)

This lesson was developed and taught by a Hawaiian teacher to inspire in her students a deep love and stewardship for the land. Kehaulani Puʻu is the Coordinator of a Hawaiian Astronomy Curriculum Development Project.

Objective: To develop positive attitudes regarding the environment by developing or increasing a sense of connection to nature.

Essential Question: How do our attitudes and perspectives of the environment affect the way we interact with nature?

Grade Level: 3rd to 5th, Ages: 7-9

Quadrant One, Right Mode: Connect (Hoʻopili)

Objective: Students will explore the concept of love of the land (alohaʻäina) by reflecting on a relationship they have with someone they love very much.

Activity: Students bring in a picture of a family member or close friend for whom they have great love and respect and use the picture to create an image to depict the bond they have with that family member/close friend. Students will share the image with the class.

Assessment: Completion of the assignment, effort and quality of picture image, and participation.

Quadrant One, Left Mode: Attend (KĀLAILAI)

Objective: Students will analyze the nature of their relationships through a large group discussion.

Activity: Students are led in a discussion by teacher. Teacher introduces the idea/concept of a bond/connection. Students are asked to think about what it is that connects them to that person. Birth? Genealogy? Caring? Teacher lists responses on the board, then reviews each one.

Teacher asks how those in the picture show and share their aloha with the student and how the student reciprocates their aloha. How do these connections translate into actions? What kinds of things do you do to and for each other? Students share examples and/or experiences of actions within their relationships.

Assessment: Participation and contributions to discussion.

Quadrant Two, Right Mode: Image (HOʻOMOEĀ)

Objective: To bring the students from personal human relationships to their relationship to the land.

Activity: Students create a visual image that represents man's relationship to nature. The image may be local, Hawaiian or global.

What role does the environment play in their lives? How do they relate to it? Do they feel connected or not?

Students post images on the wall and have a gallery walk. Teacher asks for student reactions. What was seen, what was sensed? How do students define their relationship to the environment? The larger society? Are they connected to their environment in the same way they are connected to the person in the first activity? Why or why not?

Assessment: Completion of the assignment, effort and quality of visual, and participation in large group discussion.

Quadrant Two, Left Mode: Inform (WEHEWEHE)

Objective: To begin exploring the Hawaiian relationship to the environment.

Activity: Teacher lectures on how the students were born from the land, how the environment is their livelihood, because it takes care of them just as they care for it. Teacher explains how this was the kind of bond and connectedness our küpuna (wise elders) felt to their environment and this connectedness translated into values such as mälama 'äina and aloha 'äina, (care and love for the land) which set the standard for how Hawaiians have always interacted with the environment.

Students will complete a reading with questions assignment. Teacher will lecture on the concept of aloha/mälama 'äina and its origin within the Hawaiian story.

Students will watch the video, "Treasured Values of Hawai'i", and write a brief reaction paper to the video.

Assessment: Quality and completion of assignments.

Quadrant Three, Left Mode: Practice (HO'OMA'AMA'A)

Objective: Students will further explore the Hawaiian perspectives regarding their relationship to nature.

Activity: Students research materials that exemplify and further define the Hawaiian relationship to nature, the values of aloha and/or mälama 'äina, and the notion of a bond or connectedness to nature. Students will analyze and interpret the readings.

Assessment: Assignment rubric.

Quadrant Three, Right Mode: Extend (HOʻÄKEA)

Objective: To foster an appreciation, respect and connection to the environment.

Activity: 1) Teacher will lead students in a listening exercise.
2) Students will adopt a section in the mäla (garden outside their school) as their own. They will care for and maintain this garden throughout the year. 3) Students will attend a camping trip in which different cultural experiences will be planned. Students will also prepare at least one meal using site resources.

Suggested Camping Areas: Hawaiʻi: Waipiʻo Valley, Kapoho;
Mäui: Molokaʻi: Länaʻi: Kahoʻolawe;Oʻahu: Kauaʻi:

Assessment: Participation.

Quadrant Four, Left Mode: Refine(HOʻOHAKUHIA)

Objective: To demonstrate "new-found" perspective or connection to environment.

Activity: Students will create a visual that represents their "newfound" perspective towards their environment. Students may choose a certain place if desired.

Students will also utilize what is cared for in the garden during any potential activities. Students will also share their garden when opportunity arises.

Assessment: Rubric.

Quadrant Four, Right Mode: Perform (HOʻIKE)

Objective: to share insights and newfound perspectives with others.

Activity: Assignments will be compiled into a book to be titled by the students and kept in the school library.

Assessment: Quality of completed book.

Possible Improvements to this Lesson
in Terms of "Roundness"

☆ Did this teacher help her students to see the big picture, if so, how did she do this?

☆ Decide if anything could be added to enhance the ability of the students to picture the concept, to take a systems approach.

☆ How did this teacher use roundness in this lesson?

☆ How successful was the use of roundness?

☆ Could more have been done? What and how?

☆ Now take one of your own lessons, add a roundness technique and teach the lesson with it added. Note what happens to your students. Share what happens with a peer, coach or a group.

☆ How vital is roundness to help students understand? Help each other come up with more ways to use roundness.

☆ Your activity **before** roundness enhancement:

☆ Your activity **after** roundness enhancement:

☆ What happened when you tried it?

4. Patterns

Pattern Recognition: the ability to discern similarities of form among two or more things, whether these be textile designs, facial resemblances, graphs of repeating biological growth cycles or similarities between historical epochs.

It is but a short step from pattern recognition to problem-solving.

For some the new chaos theory is the study of mathematical patterns (hidden under apparent randomness) that can be found, especially at high levels of energy, in large and complex and rapidly changing systems, such as global weather.

This sensitivity to patterns does appear to be a recurrent theme among visual thinkers.

—Thomas West

Significant learning occurs when the learner encounters discrepant events. It's the discrepancy that lets you see the pattern.

—Jerome Bruner

Examine the following lesson in terms of its use of Pattern.

Primary Science

A 4MAT lesson plan

Animal Survival: Animal Habitats

Author: David Hamaker

Students will learn the characteristic of animal habitats in the context of their survival.

Quadrant One, Right Mode

Students play hide and seek outdoors. Students are selected to find each other.

Quadrant One, Left Mode

Students in small groups answer the following questions:

> Why were students who were found last more successful at hiding?

> What makes a good hiding place?

> What are the common features of good hiding places?

> How are these features important to animals seeking safety?

Quadrant Two, Right Mode

Students go outside to use what they have learned from their list of criteria to find places where squirrels, rabbits and other animals might have good hiding places.

Quadrant Two, Left Mode

Teachers provide information and illustrations on the concepts, with videos of animal habitats.

Quadrant Three, Left Mode

Students complete worksheets, answer questions from the text.

They are also required to find animal hiding places in their own yards at home and make a list of what they find and sketch their findings.

Quadrant Three, Right Mode

Students create a life-size fictional creature, one that can be easily hidden in the classroom.

Quadrant Four, Left Mode

Students create a written description of their creature. Students in groups of four predict how successful that creature will be in hiding in the classroom.

Quadrant Four, Right Mode

Students make their paper model creatures and hide them in the classroom.

They invite another class to come in, make a brief presentation explaining the task, and then have them try to find their creatures.

Possible Improvements to this Lesson in Terms of Patterns

☆ How did this teacher use pattern-recognition in this lesson?

☆ How successful was his use of patterns?

☆ Could more have been done? What and how?

☆ Now take one of your own lessons, add a pattern-recognition technique and teach the lesson with it added. Note what happens to your students. Share what happens with a peer, coach or a group.

☆ How vital is pattern recognition to help students understand? Help each other come up with more ways to use roundness.

☆ Your activity *before* patterns enhancement:

☆ Your activity *after* patterns enhancement:

☆ What happened when you tried it?

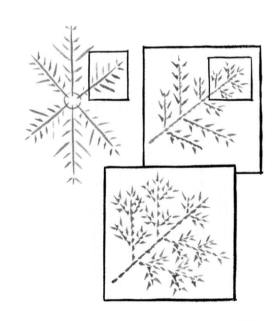

5. Graphic Organizers

Graphic organizers have been around for some time, but it is only when the right-mode research began to surface that educators realized their power for increasing understanding. The use of a visual representation of a concept, an idea, an event, or a story line illustrates not only the idea, but the spatial relationships and hence the connections between the parts.

Try using graphic organizers with all your content, and even make them part of your assessments.

☆ Practice with these and pay particular attention to the process you go through in creating them.

Create a graphic image of cause and effect.

Create a graphic to show the story line in *Little Red Riding Hood.*

Create a graphic organizer to show a sequence of events.

Share these with your peers.

☆ Now try the following:

   Use an image technique to teach the concept of community caring.

   Use a metaphor to teach how we draw conclusions.

   Use round thinking to examine the strategies used in a historical battle.

   Use patterning to teach the early explorers of this continent.

   Use a graphic organizer to teach a story line.

☆ How did this teacher use graphic organizers in this lesson?

☆ Now take one of your own lessons, add a graphic organizer technique and teach the lesson with it added. Note what happens to your students. Share what happens with a peer, coach or a group.

☆ How vital are graphic organizers to help students understand? Help each other come up with more ways to use roundness.

☆ Your activity *before* graphic organizer enhancement:

☆ Your activity *after* graphic organizer enhancement:

☆ What happened when you tried it?

Images, metaphors, the sense of the whole, patterns, and graphic organizers all can be categorized under visual and spatial thinking. Howard Gardner affords this kind of thinking special status.

Thomas West speaking of Gardner's thinking on this status:

The special status Gardner accords this mode of thought is underlined by his concluding observations about it. Gardner indicates that there is evidence that this particular mode has greater longevity in individuals, and may be associated in a fundamental way with what we know as wisdom. Here, once again, is the preoccupation with wholes, rather than parts, with patterns rather than pieces, with similarities rather than differences.

Gardner's words as quoted by West:

My own view is that each form of intelligence has a natural life course: while logical-mathematical thought proves fragile later in life, across all individuals…at least certain aspects of visual and spatial knowledge prove robust, especially in individuals who have practiced them regularly throughout their lives There is a sense of the whole, a "gestalt" sensitivity, which is central in spatial intelligence, and which seems to be a reward for aging—a continuing or perhaps even an enhanced capacity to appreciate the whole, to discern patterns even when certain details of fine points may be lost. Perhaps wisdom draws on this.

This is an amazing quote!

☆ Finish the sentence and share your conclusion with your peers.

A life of schooling with no attention to any of the aspects of visual and spatial intelligence could lead to…

Answers to the Right and Left Mode Quiz

1.T, 2.F, it triples in size, 3.T, 4.F, it lights up the left hemisphere, 5.F, they are pruned if they are not used, 6.T, 7.T, 8.F, the right does, 9.T, 10.T, 11.T, 12.F, we remember things in context, the way we are today, 13.T, 14.F, three ways, also creative, 15.T

Chapter Two

4MAT and Concepts

Conceptualize Your Content

When you design instruction with 4MAT you must conceptualize your content. You cannot create a 4MAT lesson without going through this process. You must take the content you want to teach and "umbrella" it, that is, find the connecting idea that relates to your students. For example, if you were teaching Christopher Columbus, you might identify an overarching concept of **Exploration**. Most learners of all ages love to explore or still remember when they loved to explore.

In order to find a Quadrant One experience that connects your students to the content, you must find the common ground that connects for all of them. The common ground is the concept(s) you choose. Imagine the difficulty of creating a personal connection between the learners of today and Christopher Columbus – a 15th century explorer who took months to cross the Atlantic versus two hours from New York to Paris today on the Concorde. Instead, think of hooking learners with "**Exploration**", with the courage of the astronauts, with Voyager 2, a billion miles out in space, long past Neptune and our star system, or with ways that test boundaries in their own lives. These are real connections and when connections happen, ideas flow freely.

How do we capture the essence of something? How do we come to understand the core of an idea, a book, a piece of music, or even a person? Most of us can remember an event when suddenly something became clear.

What was that about?

Imagine you have just left a movie with friends, and someone asks,

"What was that movie really about?"

And before you can answer one member of your party says,

"Betrayal, the movie was about betrayal!"

You realize this answer has cut through all the details: the sequence of events, the atmosphere the director has set so painstakingly, the cast of characters, and named precisely the core theme of the film. You are struck by the keenness of mind it takes to do that, and the artistry of the filmmaker who pulled it off.

Or consider teaching MacBeth to your students. Perhaps **Betrayal** is the core concept. You could design a lesson that would weave **Betrayal** throughout, pulling from students' personal experiences. If you are asked to consider the color red, your brain would be able to look around and see all the examples and patterns of red – in an instant. In a similar sense, you can ask learners to examine all the instances of betrayal in the play and in their lives. They will begin to see it all around them. With this simple emphasis you will have created recognition, retention, and meaning.

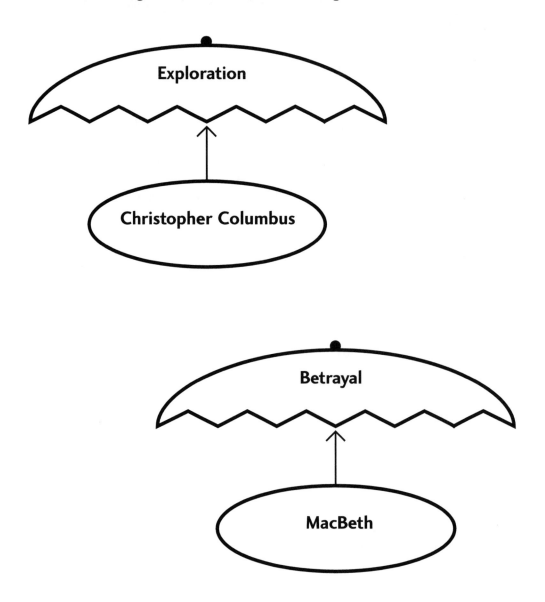

Working with Concepts

A **concept** is a significant idea that relates to other significant ideas in a way that connects to the main body of content and creates meaning for students in their lives.

A **topic** is a subset of a concept, a smaller section of content that specifies the particulars.

How do you decide which is which? How does an idea get "concept status"?

There are no hard and fast rules. The answer is, it depends.

It depends on the context, the learners, the time and place. It depends on the teacher and how well she knows her students. An idea is a concept when it naturally connects: to learners, to content and to other significant ideas. A good concept will present cross-discipline possibilities, e.g., Exploration in Science, Social Studies, Literature, Music, etc. The following pages will help you understand the difference between concepts and topics and how this applies to your teaching.

Different Teachers, Different Concepts

It is important to note that different teachers will define concepts differently, with equally good results.

In a lesson covering Romantic Poets, one teacher realized these poets were very often rebels of their times, and their poetry was an expression of need to assert their individuality. She shaped the lesson around the concept of **Individuality** and the need to be self-expressive.

Another teacher saw the common thread among the same poets as their awe of natural beauty. She decided on the concept of **Beauty** and the ways people express their appreciation of beauty and shaped the lesson around that concept.

Two teachers, with the exact same content, using different concepts, both with great results in terms of learner engagement, resonance, retention, and creative adaptation of material learned. When creating concepts, trust your own insights as to what might resonate most with your students.

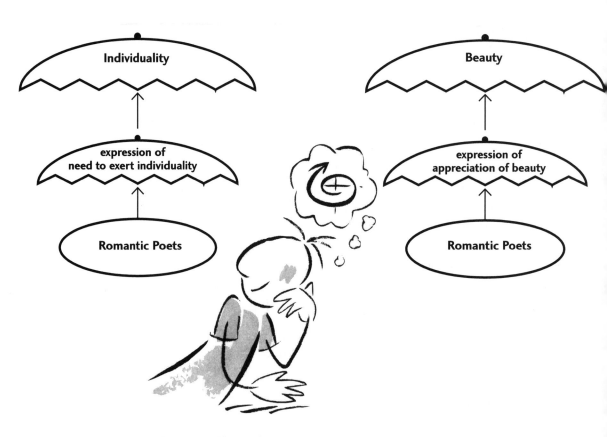

☆ See if you can distinguish between a concept and a topic. Which items would you consider **concepts** and which would you consider **topics**?

	concept	topic
Structure (as in Science)	_____	_____
Tides	_____	_____
Root words	_____	_____
Quality	_____	_____
Human systems (as in Social Studies)	_____	_____
Percentage	_____	_____
Magnets	_____	_____
The Dark Ages	_____	_____
The Civil War	_____	_____
Force	_____	_____

☆ List five concepts in any discipline you believe should be taught to all students.

1.

2.

3.

4.

5.

☆ Share these with your peer group.

One way teachers can recognize the difference between concepts and topics is by asking, "What is this a study in?" For example, you could say that **Christopher Columbus is a study in Exploration**.

☆ Keeping this in mind, consider the next list, categorized by subject areas. Play with them as concepts and also as topics. If you decide to make them topical, then name the concept they might serve.

Social Studies	Science	Math
Continuity in Human Culture	Plants	Decimals
The American Family	Energy	Functions
Basic Human Needs	Diastrophism (Movement of the Earth's Crust)	Value
Grain: Basic Food for Humanity	Solar System	Binary Systems
Arms Negotiations	UFO's	Volume
Fossil Fuels	Stars	Plane
Interdependence of Peoples	Air Pollution	Zero
First Amendment Rights	Volcanoes	Line
Environmental Influences	The Scientist	Ratio
The Migrations of People	Genetic Manipulation	Place Value
		Exponents

Literature	Parts of Speech	Music	Visual Arts
The Novel	Vowels	Rhythm	Composition
Drama as Social Criticism	Comprehension	Meter	Expression
Realism	Main Ideas	Criticism	Impressionism
Characterization	Context	Tempo	Negative Space
The Short Story	Sequencing	Jazz	Perspective
The Humorists	Consonant Blends	Impressionism	
Myth	Pattern Recognition	Rubato	
Fiction	Inferences	Counterpoint	
Literary Methods		Fugue	
Impressionism		12-Bar Blues	
Reading		Sonata Form	
Syntax		Timbre	
		Form	
		Modality	

Concepts and Standards

☆ Look at the following standards*. See if you can determine if there are concepts embedded in them that might help students establish personal connections. Choose one and work through the best conceptual approach you can envision.

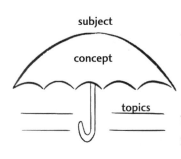

Language Arts-Writing

Uses strategies to organize written work (e.g., includes a beginning, middle, and ending; uses a sequence of events).

Language Arts-Speech

Uses content, style, and structure that is appropriate for specific audiences: that is, formal or informal language, public or private communications, with the different purposes of entertaining, influencing, or informing.

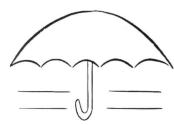

Math

Understands that some events are more likely to happen than others.

Understands that the word "chance" refers to the likelihood of an event.

Science

Knows that plants and animals progress through life cycles of birth, growth and development, reproduction, and death; the details of these life cycles are different for different organisms.

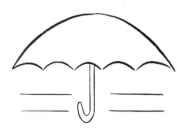

Knows that the strength of the electric force between two charged objects is proportional to the charges (opposite charges attract whereas like charges repel) and, as with gravitation, inversely proportional to the square of the distance between them.

☆ **Choose one and work through the best conceptual approach you can envision.**

---

*From the MCREL list

Umbrella as a Verb

The process we use for conceptualizing content is called **The Umbrella Exercise**. You write the description of the content you hope to teach in the oval at the bottom of the page as illustrated below and then attempt to find the overarching idea and write it into the umbrella that covers the oval. The umbrella/oval is a graphic organizer that helps clarify the best way to approach the content. The concept you choose to write in your umbrella is the idea that is implicit in the content and connects best to your students.

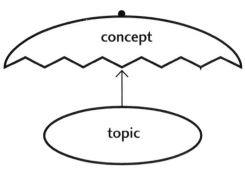

When you "umbrella" a topic, you find its **essence**. For example, photosynthesis might umbrella up to growth, equations in Algebra to balance. A lesson on the Holocaust might umbrella to dehumanization. 4MAT lessons begin with this content essence. These umbrellas can be thought of as overarching not only the content but every element of the unit. These concepts guide lesson authors and students through each step of the 4MAT process.

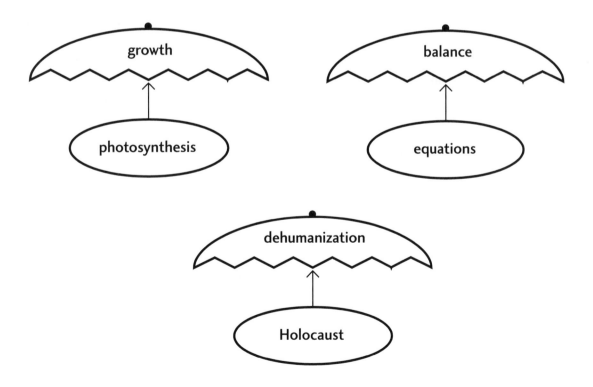

Exploration as an Example

We chose **Exploration** as an umbrella concept for Christopher Columbus.

Think of the idea of exploration. All humans have a need to break boundaries, to reach higher. All humans are intrigued by the unknown. Is the need to explore part of our makeup? What of the equally important human needs— to settle down, to build something lasting? How are these dichotomous ideas related?

Exploration is a significant idea that relates to other significant ideas in a way that connects to the main body of the Social Studies content and has great potential for creating meaning in students' lives. While there are no hard and fast rules for determining concepts, there are some guidelines.

More Practice with Umbrella Concepts

☆ The ideas below are significant enough to qualify as concepts. Does each fulfill our definition of a concept? We have filled in some sample concepts from various subject areas. Now add your ideas, based on your understanding of these subjects and your familiarity with your curriculum and standards.

Literature

Our concept is: Heroism

Our concept is: The Novel

Other significant concepts might be:

1. _____

2. _____

3. _____

Grammar

Our concept is: The Sentence

Other significant concepts might be:

1. _____

2. _____

3. _____

Writing

Our concept is: Expression

Other significant concepts might be:

1. _____

2. _____

3. _____

Music

Our concept is: Rhythm. There are great possibilities here–cycles of life, both biological and emotional, tides (using ocean sounds, day and night, seasons, etc.).

Other significant concepts might be:

1. _____

2. _____

3. _____

Math

Our concept is: Balance

Other concepts might be:

1. _____

2. _____

3. _____

Science

Our concept is: Living and Non-living Things

Other concepts might be:

1. _____

2. _____

3. _____

You are encouraged to challenge our choice of concepts. We stress the need for teachers to build their own conceptual structures to relate and organize content and standards for them. These decisions must be made in the context of their learners.

While there are significant ideas in any content area that are basic to understanding that content, there are also many choices that can be made, choices that will form meaningful connections for particular students in particular places in particular times. Even in the current climate of micro-management of curriculum, these choices must be left to master teachers.

4MAT in Action!

What are the Concepts that Overarch the Things You Teach?

Now look at lessons you are currently teaching or developing. Think about them in terms of 4MAT. These sections will build upon each other. So work completed in this section, for example, carries over to the next section. Have your lessons in front of you as you perform these exercises.

☆ For each of the units you are working on, complete the concept-finding worksheet below.

Concept-Finding Worksheet

"What's Important Here?"

1. What is the lesson's title?

2. What is the lesson about?

3. Does the above definition capture the very essence of the lesson? If not, think about what ideas might overarch your response above and experiment with those ideas using the following queries.

4. Is that a significant idea?

5. Does it relate to other significant ideas in a way that connects to the main body of the content?

6. Does it have potential for creating meaning in students' lives?

7. What is it a study in? The harder this is, the bigger your ideas may be. If, for example, you decide that Exploration is a study in Exploration, you're on the right track.

8. In what ways do your students encounter this regularly? Are their lives or the lives of their family and friends touched by it?

9. What would happen if it didn't exist? Would that be a problem?

10. Does it relate to other ideas in other subjects? All the most important ideas touch every corner of every subject (and human endeavor). A good concept will have numerous associations to other areas of life and study.

11. How would your students be personally effected by an internalization of this concept–not just knowing about it, but having it be a part of them?

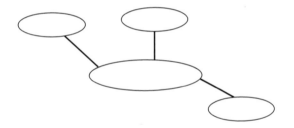

12. How would it look in the center of a mindmap? A good concept makes a good hub for a mindmap. Try it! Sketch a quick associative map of your main idea in the space below. Doodle your concept mindmap here. Feel free to add balloons.

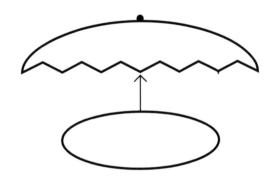

13. Most importantly, if you feel that your unit essence is not quite big enough, don't sweat it. Come up with some other ideas that you feel *do* overarch your unit. If you're wrong, you'll discover later that the main concept choice may need tweaking, as you try to connect to learners in Quadrant One, for example. Umbrella your concept here.

Relating Concepts to Instruction

Consider the graphic below as you consider the relationship of concepts and topics to your 4MAT units. Note that the reason for concept-based teaching lies in the first step of 4MAT, where learners are actively engaged. Note also that the topic of your unit can be placed in Quadrant Two, Left Mode, the telling place. Throughout the unit the concept will be reinforced, culminating with a performance and integration component in Quadrant Four.

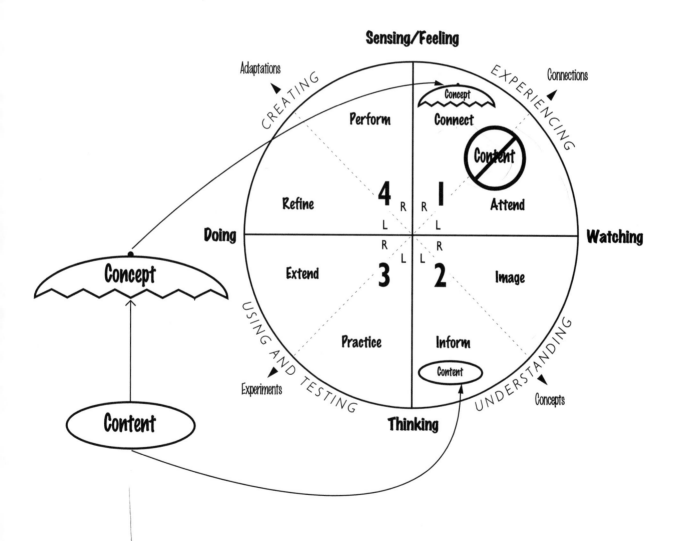

Chapter Three

A Deeper Look at Quadrant One

Quadrant One—The Reason for the Learning

The reason for learning the material must be clear to the students. How you merge what you know about them with your content knowledge is the key to motivating them. The way you bring these two together, the student and the content, is crucial to your teaching success.

Why is Quadrant One So Difficult?

Because we have to connect the material to be learned to the students personally and we have not been taught to do that. Teaching is assumed to be primarily telling. The dialogue part of teaching was supposed to happen after we had given our students enough knowledge so they could carry on some kind of dialogue. The supposition has always been that our students did not know the content we knew, or else why would we be teaching it to them? And of course, that is true, they do not know the content in the way we need them to, and they are not experienced enough sometimes to even know they do not know.

So what actually is the purpose of Quadrant One? We believe it is the key to all learning.

Others question whether or not it is even necessary.

It is helpful here to pause and examine the thinking of those who question the need for Quadrant One at all. Examine some of their thoughts concerning this issue.

Take this question regarding teaching a skill:

> If you are teaching a skill, a medical procedure for example, how to give a shot, how to take blood, do you really need a "**WHY?**"

Our answer:

> Would it be a good thing if the technician knew why?
>
> Why…
>
> Why she was taking blood at all?
>
> Why this procedure is the one best way to do it?
>
> Why it might be dangerous to do it incorrectly?
>
> Why most patients are squeamish about the procedure?
>
> Why any procedure that invades the body causes emotional reactions in patients

Their response:

> And if all the above are true, why not just cover it all in the lecture?
>
> Why not just tell the students why?
>
> Why go to the trouble of having your students discover for themselves the **Why** of the content?

☆ What is your response? Talk this over with a small group of peers. Write your thoughts here. Ask the same question about teaching sports. Try it with tennis, golf or basketball.

Think of a skill associated with any sport and examine whether it would help in the attainment of fluid expertise in that skill to have potential athletes discover "**Why**" themselves. If their coaches tell them why, or even ignore the necessity for discussing the why at all in the belief that mastery will bring the understanding, would that be just as good?

☆ What is your response, does Quadrant One work in sports?

☆ Try it with a math algorithm. (a logical step-by-step procedure for solving a problem) Isn't it just a procedure that has to be learned in order to move on to more difficult procedures? How does understanding the meaning of a basic math operation help?

☆ After sharing your thoughts with some of your fellow teachers, complete the following sentences.

What if the math teacher really believed that learners would be better equipped to do math if they knew the Whys. How might she start to teach an algorithm? (Take simple addition or subtraction.)

What if the math teachers began with…

What if a coach believed that a certain way of performing a skill needed to be understood by athletes at the "**Why**" level. How might he teach dribbling in basketball?

What if the coach began with…

Do you think a medical instructor could set up a discovery exercise based on the learning steps of those who created the procedure in the first place—the insights that led to the necessity for the procedure, the decision about the best way to do it, the kinds of things that initially went wrong as they experimented with the procedure? How might that be done? And if it could be done what kind of enhanced expertise would result?

What if the medical instructor began with…

Leading Students to Personal Learning Connections

Remember when you had to learn the names of the 50 capitals of the 50 states?

What connections did you have to this task?

None, I suspect.

Put that kind of information into a category that Einstein described as "the things that clutter up the mind".

> *"But in physics, I soon learned to scent out the paths that led to the depths, and to disregard everything else, all the many things that clutter up the mind, and divert it from the essential...*
>
> *the hitch in this was, of course, the fact that one had to cram all of this stuff into one's mind for the examination, whether one liked it or not."*

Why should you need to know the capitals of the fifty states when the Internet could handle that for you with the click of a finger?

On the other hand, what connection might you be able to make for your students regarding the capital city of their state?

Could you interest a group of students in the reasons why a particular site in the state was chosen for the capital? Was it geography or river access, for example, when the rivers were the main highways? Or was it hub access, a location right in the center of things? Or was it railroad access that made the decision? Or was it the convenience of the folks with power and money who decided where the capital should be based on their needs?

These questions have potential for intriguing students. The students would have interesting experiences as they searched for the answers. Think of the connections to their own lives.

They have to commute to work.

They need access to shopping.

They need inexpensive transportation.

They need to get to good schools.

And they need to understand issues of power.

Given that they were in charge of the decision, what would they have to know to make it meaningful.

These issues are present in all our lives, even young lives. The trick is to connect them to the learning, to make it significant.

Quadrant One is key to significant learning. It connects the experiences of students to the learning journey their teacher plans for them. A well done Quadrant One motivates! It takes students on a journey they did not even know would interest them at the outset.

☆ Create an interesting way to begin a unit on the capital city of your state, one that would really intrigue whatever level learners you teach.

Three Ideas

1.

2.

3.

The Right and Left Modes of Quadrant One

The **Right Mode** of Quadrant One is a happening, not a telling.

The telling comes later.

The Right Mode is an emotional experience, one that engages the heart.

This includes humor, recognition ("I know that"), resonance ("Ah, yes, I've been there"), intrigue ("Hmm-hmm-hmm, how interesting") and any and all of the above.

Eyes narrow to slits,

focus zeroes in,

attention is strong,

students are connected.

This learning is more than a passing interest, it is focused.

And it is every teacher's dream.

If you are a master teacher, you have worked endlessly at pulling off this kind of thing.

The key word is **intrinsic**—wholly within, an essential element, occurring for its own sake, not for any consequences.

The opposite of intrinsic is extrinsic—not an essential part, coming from the outside.

So much of instructional design is extrinsic.

If and when extrinsic instruction becomes part of the learner, the teacher has done both.

But so many times it is "In one ear and out the other".

Intrinsic is valuing the learning for its own sake.

This is the purpose of the **Connect** of Quadrant One.

The connect of Quadrant One, Right Mode touches them in a way that awakens something in them, arouses an eagerness that intrigues, imparts value.

The students must be engaged at the feeling level.

Flow: *a state of grace known as "the zone" where excellence becomes effortless, a blissful, steady absorption in the moment.*

—Mihaly Csikszentmihalyi

Daniel Goleman states that being able to enter flow is emotional intelligence at its best, harnessing the emotions in the service of learning. It is self-forgetfulness, with responses being perfectly attuned to the changing demands of the task.

Goleman goes on to describe how children attain mastery.

"The flow model suggests that achieving mastery of any skill or body of knowledge should ideally happen naturally, as the child is drawn to the areas that spontaneously engage her—that, in essence, she loves. That initial passion can be the seed for high levels of attainment, as the child comes to realize that pursuing the field—whether it be dance, math, or music—is a source of the joy of flow. And since it takes pushing the limits of one's ability to sustain flow, that becomes a prime motivator for getting better and better; it makes the child happy. This, of course, is a more positive model of learning and education than most of us encountered in school. Who does not recall school at least in part as endless dreary hours of boredom punctuated by moments of high anxiety? Pursuing flow through learning is a more humane, natural, and very likely more effective way to marshal emotions in the service of education."

To create this kind of instructional eagerness the teacher must be in touch with both the students and the content.

Why do teachers have such a difficult time creating positive emotional right-mode teaching strategies?

Three Reasons

1.

2.

3.

The **Left Mode** of Quadrant One on the other hand is a stepping back, a stopping, a pause, an examination. What just happened? How do you see this? What made you recognize/resonate with what just happened? What are you intrigued to find out? Are you seeing the problem more clearly and understanding how problems like this necessitate the learning we are about to pursue?

Sharing perceptions, feelings, thoughts and reactions is an integral part of Quadrant One, Left Mode. So are:

> Listing commonalities
>
> Recording differing perceptions
>
> Analyzing the parts
>
> Objectifying the experience, no longer in it, but out of it and examining it.

It is metacognitive.

"**Metacognition**—the ability to think about how one thinks, pondering the factors that influence your thinking."

☆ Create three ways in Quadrant One, Left Mode to encourage metacognition in your students.

Here's an example:

> The students have just told one another stories of events in their lives that connect to the teacher's concept. Then they are asked to list the commonalities in their stories. They are asked to comment on whether or not they recognized their feelings in the stories of their fellow students. Thinking about how we think—metacognition.

Three Examples

1.

2.

3.

WHAT IS META-COGNITION?

META = Greek root meaning "beside" COGNITION: from a Latin root meaning "to know" - The mental process or faculty of knowing, including aspects such as awareness, perception, reasoning, and judgment. You won't find it in the dictionary, but it's frequently used in education. We define it as thinking about how you're thinking (or knowing). It describes a self-analysis, a self-monitoring, an understanding of your own cognitive processes. Asking learners to think about their thinking is a very powerful tool for deepening understanding of any idea.

Chapter Three: A Deeper Look at Quadrant One

4MAT in Action!

Doing Quadrant One

Now consider the major units you identified in the Concepts exercise from the previous chapter.

Throughout this workbook, we will "throw things up on the wheel", which refers to examining instruction in light of the 4MAT framework and placing the elements of your lessons in the appropriate 4MAT quadrants and octants. It is helpful to have your lessons in front of you as you perform these exercises.

Step One: What's Already There?

It's likely that there are already elements of Quadrant One in your units. Throw them on the wheel! Do you have an activity designed to engage learners at the feeling level? Do you ask them to consider the **WHY** of your content, for example, "Why is this important to know?" Do you set them up with a situation that intrigues and leaves them eager for content to come?

*Important note: If an activity involves "telling" on the part of the teacher, it probably does **not** belong in Quadrant One.*

Think experiential, something happens.

Think of lots of images lying about that can be chosen in silence, then help the students connect them to the concept.

Think "talk-story" where students relate past experiences around a concept.

Think problems that are analogous to the skills you want them to master.

Think small cooperative groups of students.

Think scenarios that could really take place.

Think about examples from today.

Think of the absence of something you are about to teach.

Think music: here's an example, three different versions of *Somewhere Over the Rainbow*: Eva Cassidy's, Willie Nelson's and Judy Garland's as a beginning to a unit on "**Voice**"—learning to speak in our own voice.

Think Right Mode.

Think process.

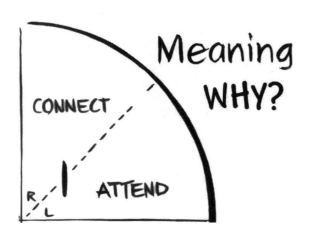

Meaning
WHY?

CONNECT

R
L

ATTEND

☆ Using the diagram on the following page, jot down those elements of your unit that seem to fit in Quadrant One. Refer to the diagram below for help with this alignment. What elements of Quadrant One are already present in your unit?

One Right–Connect

One Left–Attend

Chapter Three: A Deeper Look at Quadrant One

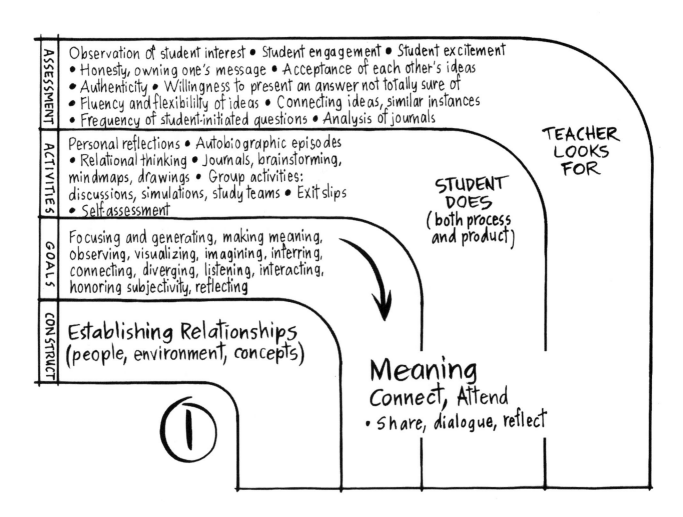

ASSESSMENT
Observation of student interest • Student engagement • Student excitement
• Honesty, owning one's message • Acceptance of each other's ideas
• Authenticity • Willingness to present an answer not totally sure of
• Fluency and flexibility of ideas • Connecting ideas, similar instances
• Frequency of student-initiated questions • Analysis of journals

ACTIVITIES
Personal reflections • Autobiographic episodes
• Relational thinking • Journals, brainstorming,
mindmaps, drawings • Group activities:
discussions, simulations, study teams • Exit slips
• Self-assessment

GOALS
Focusing and generating, making meaning,
observing, visualizing, imagining, inferring,
connecting, diverging, listening, interacting,
honoring subjectivity, reflecting

CONSTRUCT
Establishing Relationships
(people, environment, concepts)

TEACHER
LOOKS
FOR

STUDENT
DOES
(both process
and product)

①

Meaning
Connect, Attend
• Share, dialogue, reflect

Step Two: How Can You Enhance What's There?

In Quadrant One, consider the reasons for teaching the concept and design an opening activity based on those reasons. The activity you ultimately choose must capture the attention of students.

It should provoke discussion

It should be interactive.

It must relate to their lives.

It needs to contain something that is already familiar to them.

For each of your developing units, state the immediate personal value of the concept you identified for *all* students *now* (not in their future).

You need to find the value that will connect the material to your students' lives. You need to hook into their interest in the content, into what they already know. Consider again, the concept of Exploration. How is this of immediate personal value to students? Does this differ depending on the age of the student? Here are some answers (there can be many).

> It helps them understand themselves better, to discover it is human to explore, test and break boundaries.
>
> It is important to understand how to respond to this human need (and the companion need to have shelter and security).
>
> It's OK to be fearful when venturing out into the unknown.
>
> It takes courage to go first.
>
> It's important to appreciate the courage personified by explorers.
>
> There are many ways and many things to explore.

Think of the student in every class, the one who inevitably raises his hand asking, "Why do we need to know this?", and answer him!

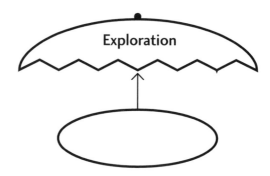

Chapter Three: A Deeper Look at Quadrant One

 **Quadrant One Worksheet: Why, Oh Why?**

1. What is the unit's title?

2. What is the unit's concept?

3. Does it have potential for creating meaning in students' lives?

4. In what way do your students encounter this regularly? Are their lives or the lives of their family and friends touched by it?

5. What would happen if it didn't exist? Would that be a problem?

6. In what ways might you demonstrate its importance? How can they be made to *feel* its importance at a personal level?

7. How might you demonstrate the problems that would arise if it didn't exist?

8. In what ways might you get students to reflect on what they already know about it, either intuitively or directly?

9. What examples of it exist *today*? What elements of it exist in current events?

A Bushel Basket of Quadrant One Activities

Consider the following list of opening activities for lessons. They will offer ideas for how to engage learners in Quadrant One.

High School Science

Students bring to class one living and one non-living thing.

Students "experience" a jar of rotting potatoes, noting texture, color, smell, etc. The content is Decay.

Students view a clip from "*Crossing Delancy*" in which an old-fashioned matchmaker brings a "nice boy" and a "good girl" together at the kitchen table. While the couple interacts, the matchmaker leaves them alone. (This content of this lesson is Enzymes. The metaphor: girl and boy are substrates brought together so they can react. They may have gotten together eventually but it might have taken seventy years. The kitchen table is the active site and the matchmaker leaves and does not become a part of the final reaction.)

High School Math

Students line up and do "the wave" (popularized at football games). They bring in pictures and physical examples of waves in nature. They share examples of waves they've found in the world. The content is graphing sinusoids.

High School Social Studies

Students experience injustice in the classroom. "Riches" are scattered about the classroom. After they are harvested, it is clearly unfair. The lesson continues as they visualize the incompatibility between the political ideals of liberty and slavery.

Middle School Social Studies

Students are split into family units and are assigned an income. They are asked to design a budget appropriate to the community where they live. They are then told that all income will stop abruptly and must modify and prioritize their budget drastically. The content is The Great Depression.

This one is set up in advance. After students settle in, the teacher moves to encroach on a student's space–sitting/standing too close.

The teacher asks the student if he feels crowded. This role play is scripted to demonstrate a reaction of one who is having his personal boundaries violated. The content: geographic boundaries.

Middle School Science

Students gather around a "mystery box" and without touching it identify five things that could not be in the box and five that could. They go on to form hypotheses about the contents of the box. The content here is scientific method.

Middle/High School Math

Outdoors, students fire a toy cannon at a target. Content: Cartesian coordinate system.

Intermediate Social Studies

Five students participate in a game. Choose some aggressive and some more timid students. Other students observe. The object is to have four or five dice show the same number. The prize is a piece of candy. There are no rules except that when the teacher says, "Stop" all action must freeze. Observers are to note the reactions of the players. Afterward, the players each express their feelings, eventually coming around to the need for rules so the aggressive people don't take over the game. This lesson goes on to rules and governance.

Intermediate Science

Students engage in a traditional bobbing for apples activity. Discussion after the activity focuses on what makes it so difficult for people to poke their heads underwater, how would we have to be built differently to make us better at it? Introduce concept of adaptation. The lesson's content: birds and bird adaptation.

Intermediate Science/Social Studies

Half of the students in the class are placed in a physically handicapping position for part of the day, i.e., taped fingers and thumb, preferred arm in a sling, crutches, one leg made to be longer than the other, blindfolded, earplugs, mouth taped shut, etc. Buddies assist. Later the handicapped and the buddies reverse roles. The content: adaptation and survival (though this could have gone in many different directions).

Intermediate Language Arts

Students build a submarine sandwich, taking note of the main ingredients as they go. The content is Parts of Speech.

In teams, students decode special "pictorially coded" messages. They later discuss sign language, Cunieform, Hieroglyphics, Semetic writing, the Phoenician, Greek and Roman alphabets.

Intermediate Math

Students wear numbers around their necks. Three circles are drawn with masking tape at the front of the room, each large enough to fit no more than nine students. Over the circles, on the blackboard are 1's, 10's and 100's columns. The first nine students take their places in the 1's circle. When the tenth student attempts to join them, some gentle nudging occurs as they notice he won't fit! He gets booted to the 10's column. You can play around with this making all kinds of interesting numbers on the board. Content: Place Value.

Primary Language Arts

Students are divided into two groups. All the children take off their shoes and put them in a group pile. Then they have a race to see which group can identify their shoes and put them back on without talking. They then create a list of words that describe how they found their shoes – by size, color, design, which cartoon character, etc. Content: Adjectives.

Primary

The teacher keeps all the trash for one week. At the beginning of class on Monday, she dumps it all on the floor. Students look through and brainstorm how much of it could be reused. The content: recycling.

Primary Science

Students play hide and seek outdoors. What made successful hiders successful? What are the common features of good hiding places? The content: Animal habitats.

Adult Learners

Learners begin by creating a circle in the center of a piece of paper, then in mindmap fashion make a list of all the things they are or wish to be connected to. Content: Introduction to the Internet.

Create a scenario. A friend admits plagiarism of an article in order to make appointment to the Law Review. The group must choose what they would do if (1) they were not involved except as a fellow student (2) they were editors of the Review (3) their article was chosen *after* the plagiarized article. Content: Attorney/Client confidentiality.

Some Lessons to Examine in Terms of "Oneness"

Examine how the following teachers created the "**Why?**" that led their students to meaning. These are activities teachers hoped would enhance the motivation of students to value the content for its own sake.

Note how they constructed their right- and left-mode activities to amplify these reactions.

Then examine, discuss and possibly improve the Quadrant One, Right and Left Mode activities in each of these lessons.

Here are some questions to consider before you begin:

Have the activities connected the students to the content?

Have the activities initiated a feeling response?

Have these activities created any emotional reactions to the material to be learned?

How well has "telling" been avoided, instead engaging the students in dialogue?

Have they shared their reactions based on past experiences?

The first three steps of the lesson (Quadrant One, Right and Left Modes and Quadrant Two, Right Mode) are described in detail. The activities in the other five steps, are described in less detail as they are not necessary for our purpose here. You are given enough information to know where the teacher hoped to go.

☆ How might you and your small group improve the Quadrant One of these lessons? Look at the scaling descriptions we use in Level Two Training. See what your group can add.

Scaling Criteria

0 = suitable   1 = enriched   2 = Wow!

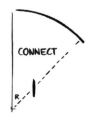

Quadrant One Right Mode

0 The activity connects learners to the concept in a personal way and directly relates to the concept.

+1 Goes to the heart. Allows students to feel their way in a deeper, richer way, an emotional (heartfelt) connect.

+2 The experience has a high personal growth potential beyond the immediate experience, and uses more than 1 modality.

Quadrant One Left Mode

0 Linked to 1R. Feelings about the experience are shared. Dialogue is lively between and among the learners.

+1 Students further explore stated feelings in some way, e.g., listing, patterning, prioritizing, stating their own goals/objectives for learning.

+2 Small group interactive learning activity where students analyze their collective experiences and produce a group "product."

Primary Mathematics

A 4MAT lesson plan

Concept: Classification by Attributes

Author: Kathleen Woodruff

Author's Remarks: Sorting, grouping and classifying is a skill that uses and strengthens logical thinking. Grouping involves awareness of attributes, which are observed and then isolated. Students need awareness of and practice in this skill in order to make sense out of things. They need to understand things grow in complexity. In this lesson we start with single, opposite groupings, and move on to more complex classifications of 8 to 16 groupings. Materials are simple and the teaching strategies engage lots of thinking, questioning and discussion.

Quadrant One, Right Mode

Objective: To initiate classification by involving students in sorting activities that interest them.

Activity: Teacher introduces game, "What's my Rule?" Teacher explains he is thinking of a rule and the class must figure out what it is. The teacher begins to separate the children into two groups. *"John go to the front of the room. Sam to the back. Linda to the front, I wonder where Sally should go?"*

Children respond, but teacher does not share the rule until all children have been sorted. They discuss the system the teacher used. When they get to the answer the teacher then tells them now they get to play the game and they get to come up with their own rule.

Children play "What's my Rule?" Four children go out of the room. The remaining children decide on a rule for sorting themselves into two groups. When the outside children return they begin asking questions. *"Would I be in that group?"* and so on until the children have figured it out. Continue playing several more times.

Assessment: Student participation through questions, guesses and general enthusiasm.

Quadrant One, Left Mode

Objective: To focus student attention on specific attributes used in the games and to list those attributes.

Activity: Using large chart paper, list the attributes used in the games in pairs.

Assessment: Student ability to understand the list and the pairing of attributes.

Quadrant Two, Right Mode

Objective: To observe objects and see the attributes. To compare two objects and understand similarities and differences.

Activity: Using Activity Blocks hold up one at a time. Elicit responses as to the attributes of each block, color, shape, etc. Hold up two blocks for comparison of differences and similarities. Allow students to work in pairs, manipulating the blocks to solve problems stated by the teacher. *"Sort by shapes, how many groups, sort by colors, how many groups?"*

Then returning to people grouping, students practice sorting through teacher direction. *"Make two groups, what rule did you use for your groups?"*

Assessment: The verbal responses and manipulation of groups with reasoning behind the classifications.

Quadrant Two, Left Mode

Objective: To teach classification using several attributes.

Activity: Sorting of many different buttons with appropriate work sheets.

Teacher keeps sorting the buttons into smaller and smaller groups by size, then shape, then color, then number of holes.

Quadrant Three, Left Mode

Objective: To practice and reinforce.

Activity: Prepared worksheets and bags of objects. Students are instructed to sort and to record their groupings.

Quadrant Three, Right Mode

Objective: To personalize the skill by collecting their own objects for sorting.

Quadrant Four, Left Mode

Objective: To give the opportunity for creative application by sorting collected objects into smaller and smaller groups.

Quadrant Four, Right Mode

Objective: To share their final classification system, with a return to the game "What's My Rule?"

☆ Possible Ways to Improve this Lesson

A 4MAT lesson plan

Intermediate Science

Concept: The Water Cycle

Author: Robbie Porter

Author's Remarks: This lesson provides an opportunity to merge art and science. When art activities are integrated into the learning of important concepts, the experience becomes richer.

Quadrant One, Right Mode

Objective: To raise student awareness as to the presence of moisture in their lives.

Activity: Have the students go outside and find moisture. Tell them to be conscious of the evidence of moisture in any of its forms, liquid, gas or vapor. Allow enough time for them to get to some of the more subtle instances of moisture.

Repeat the activity several different times during the day. Consider using an audio tape of water sounds as well.

Assessment: The success of the students in finding multiple examples of moisture.

Quadrant One, Left Mode

Objectives: To enable students to experience the variety of ways to gather information; to examine the many instances of moisture in their world; to listen to the ingenuity of their fellow students and appreciate how ideas come together and can bring a synthesis.

Activity: Have students both list and draw on large chart paper in small groups what they found. The teacher draws attention to the synthesis.

Assessment: The quality of their lists and their listening engagement.

Quadrant Two, Right Mode

Objective: To experience the water cycle, to visualize.

Activity: Teachers takes the students on a guided, imaginary tour. They are particles of water in a water cycle. Students then draw their journey.

Assessment: Their understanding as shown in their drawings.

Quadrant Two, Left Mode

Objective: Students will learn about the water cycle.

Activity: Lecture covering forms of water, sources, change processes.

Assessment: Test questions on the key points of the lecture.

Quadrant Three, Left Mode

Activity: Students label the parts of an illustrated water cycle.

Quadrant Three, Right Mode

Activity: Students create their own water cycles with visual, kinesthetic or musical media.

Quadrant Four, Left Mode

Activity: Students scale their creations using an agreed-upon rubric they have created with the teacher.

Quadrant Four, Right Mode

Activity: Cycles are performed or posted or played for another class, in a science fair or on a parent night.

☆ Possible Ways to Improve this Lesson

Chapter Four

More Help With Quadrant Two

Quadrant Two—What We Already Know

It is about the past, the knowledge of and the work done in the past.

It is our history, our heritage, our cultures, our growth and development.

It is what has already happened.

It is what we think about what has already happened.

It is the direction we are going in now.

It is vitally important.

Think of your favorite teachers.

They knew so much.

They connected things that were happening now with things that had happened.

They made it come alive for you.

I guarantee they connected it, to yesterday, to today and to your tomorrow.

Quadrant Two is the telling time.

It is monological.

But it is not the deadly blah, blah,blah.

It is reading the best experts, hearing the lecture with all the pertinent information (not the trivial stuff).

It is specific, concise and yet related to larger issues.

It must be presented conceptually.

The details must relate coherently to the structure.

The opportunity to master what the experts know and say happens in a variety of ways:

>   lectures with accompanying notes, delivered in sections that can be mastered,

>   computer reviews,

>   assignments with work study groups,

>   and sometimes, with a very adroit teacher, the dialogue becomes interactive and real.

The Right and Left Modes of Quadrant Two

The Right Mode of Quadrant Two is conceptual. It is a preparation for the telling. Here is the place where the learner images the concept. The image is based on the learner's experience.

The traditional lecture time of teaching was not concerned with any learner past experiences, they were not honored. The assumption was that the learners did not know enough yet. The tradition of the lecture was based on getting the information into the person's head, not pulling any images from the learner's previous knowing.

Consider this wonderful example:

> In a poetry lesson on Robert Frost's *The Mending Wall*, the teacher asked the students to draw instances in their lives where they were "walled in" or "walled out".
>
> Frost begins, *"There is something in me that doesn't like a wall."*
>
> Do we assume the students have no knowledge of walls?
>
> Or rather do all of us have many instances of walls in our lives?
>
> Does asking students to ponder examples from their own lives of being walled in or walled out prepare them in a very real way to experience Frost's reaction to walls?
>
> Is this better than just getting right into the poem? Why or why not?

In the third step of 4MAT you are looking for a way to bring the subjective knowing of the learner to the content.

Think **Image**—step three of 4MAT.

You can get to images with metaphors where one thing is used to represent another, a powerful teaching tool.

When students represent the concept as they have experienced it, they bring a part of themselves into the new knowledge.

Using a nonverbal media lends to reflection.

A teacher working on the Reconstruction of the South after the Civil War has students listen to period music, observe slides and then find photos of total devastation from that time and post it alongside a current photo of devastation of their choosing. They then write their feelings after imagining themselves spending an hour in one of those photos.

☆ What is this teacher after with this activity? How does it help to bring the subjectivity of the learner to the content, exploring why the Reconstruction of the South was so fraught with anger, fear and frustration?

The Right Mode of Quadrant Two and the Bridge Element of Umbrellas

In chapter one, you looked at ways to uncover the ideas that overarch a topic, using the Umbrella metaphor. Typically, when looking at topics this way, there will be a middle tier, which we identify as the **Bridge**. For example, Christopher Columbus did not umbrella *directly* to Exploration. When brainstorming what concept might overarch Columbus, we came up with many middle tier or bridge ideas. Look at the examples below to get a sense of this.

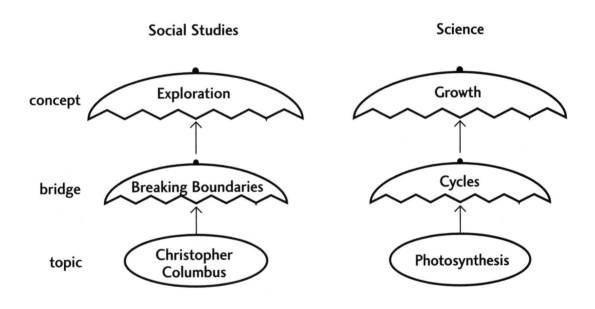

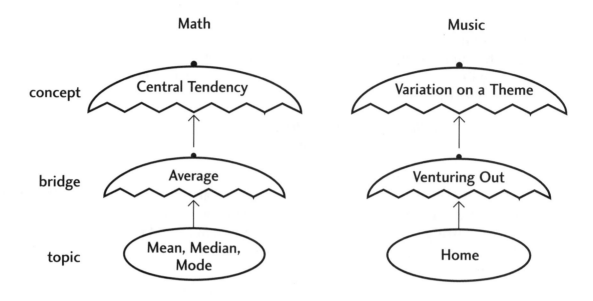

Math

Music

concept — Central Tendency · Variation on a Theme

bridge — Average · Venturing Out

topic — Mean, Median, Mode · Home

Very often, teachers struggle with the Quadrant Two, Right-mode step. We tell teachers to allow students to explore the broader perspective nonverbally, but they often need guidance in terms of the subject of the image. The bridge offers that guidance. In a lesson on the Bill of Rights, the overarching concept was Democracy. The bridge was the need for rules. These fourth graders then depicted what a world with no rules would look like.

In a lesson on Romantic poetry, the concept was Individuality. The bridge was Expressions of Rebellion, which the high school students examined by listening to and analyzing popular music.

In our Photosynthesis example above, the concept is Growth and the bridge is Cycles. You could ask learners to identify and draw examples of cycles in the world around them (including the Natural world). Some of the students will inevitably think of Seasons, creating a "teachable moment".

In the musical example above, the bridge is Venturing Out. You could ask students to consider the ways that they "test" various emerging aspects of their personalities as they grow, inevitably returning "home from their variation on a personal theme".

The Left Mode of Quadrant Two—The Telling Time

It takes learners to the heart of conceptual information, facts that relate to the core of the content. A good stand-up lecture in a relatively short time span, 30 to 40 minutes, can be a real joy in the hands of a teacher who knows the content, is passionate about it, and connects it to broader contexts.

"You know this is like…"

"Another example of this is…"

"There are five other instances of this same phenomenon…"

"And here is a most interesting point…"

The following strategies are all key parts of Left Mode, Quadrant Two:

All the students on the same page with high student focus

Laughter and humor

Images that illustrate the ideas

Demonstrations that clarify

Tools in the hands of students so they can practice what they are hearing, i.e. a teacher who presents the definition of simple machines while the students are working in a programmed way with *LegoTechnics*

Careful attention to note taking skills, using both left- and right-mode techniques

Honoring questions

Forming groups where students have to come up with the "big question" based on what they are hearing

Listening, recording, analyzing, questioning for clarification

Objectifying the knowledge, examining it

What evidence, whose perspective, how do we know?

☆ Think about and discuss with your fellow teachers how to make your lectures more demonstrative both visually and aurally.

Three Ideas

1.

2.

3.

Chapter Four: More Help With Quadrant Two

More Ways to Enhance Quadrant Two, Left Mode

Be willing to examine all sides of a topic.

Be patient with complexity. Difficult problems rarely have obvious solutions. Complex topics are multifaceted; they must to be turned over in our minds so that we can see them from a variety of angles.

Some examples:

Divide the class into teams for informal "debates" (teams prepare outside of class or one class period prior to the debate).

Use the "pass the folder" discussion format: each small group gets a folder representing a different aspect of an issue, they discuss it for a few minutes and record their contributions. Then students pass folders to the next group, repeating the process. At the end, the group holding the folder reports back to the large group.

Have students share individual concept maps in groups and write a group concept map.

Encourage students to comment on their classmates' responses before summarizing or moving to another question.

Avoid repeating an answer. Let students assume responsibility for the accuracy and audibility of their comments.

When a student asks a good question, turn it back to the class to answer. If the class answers the question, then let the answer stand and move on. Don't undercut their efforts by re-answering the question as though there is only one right answer.

Avoid dead-end questions that require only a yes/no response. Avoid programmed-answer questions that have a single, usually one-word answer. Avoid fuzzy questions that do not contain the clarity of a directed question. For example, "What do you think about the changing seasons?"

Encourage students to paraphrase.

Look at hypotheticals, for example "What would the world look like if Germany defeated the US in World War II?"

Ask follow-ups Why? Do you agree? Can you elaborate? Tell me more. Can you give an example?

Survey the class, "How many people agree with the author's point of view?" (thumbs up, thumbs down).

Provide thinking time after a question and after each response.

Utilize think-pair-share.

Play devil's advocate.

Require students to defend their reasoning against different points of view.

Let students develop their own questions.

In one successful method for leading a class discussion, the instructor acts as facilitator and scribe, eliciting suggestions from students and writing their ideas on the board. While writing students' responses on the board, you can pattern and organize ideas by putting them in different columns and categories, or drawing lines to show links.

4MAT in Action!

Doing Quadrant Two

Now consider the developing units you worked with in the previous 4MAT in Action segments.

Step One
What's Already There? The Right Mode Step

It's likely there are elements of Quadrant Two already in your units. This is especially true for Quadrant Two. Throw them on the wheel!

Because of the twofold nature of Quadrant Two, each step must be treated individually. In Quadrant Two, Right Mode, a bridge is created between the learner and the content. Here, learners creatively express their intuitive understanding of a concept. Scan your lessons for elements of *nonverbal* expression. If there are *none*, don't worry too much. This is a difficult step on the 4MAT cycle and we will guide you through it.

What's Already There? The Left Mode Step

It should be easy to spot the Quadrant Two, Left Mode aspects of your units. Think back to your original umbrella concepts. The Quadrant Two, Left Mode material is where you began before you defined the essence of the unit: Christopher Columbus, Photosynthesis, Balance in equations, Romantic poets, etc. This is the information you will be presenting to students.

Find all the elements of your units that involve telling, expert knowledge or information. These take many forms: textbooks, lecture, notes, web research, videos and many types of software (interactive software probably belongs in the Quadrant Three **Practice** portion of a unit). A special note on video. A video by itself is *not* a right-brain activity. Most educational videos are informational and not at all interactive.

The bottom-line test is this: if learners are listening, watching, or reading, consider it a Quadrant Two, Left Mode.

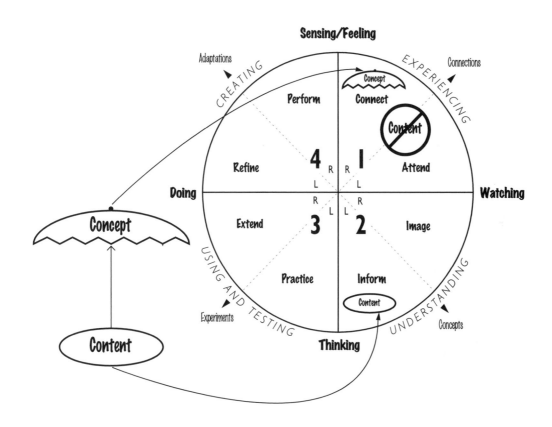

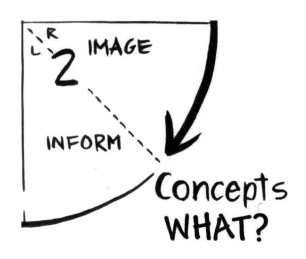

☆ Using the diagram, jot down those elements of your unit that seem to fit in Quadrant Two. Refer to the diagram for help with this alignment. What elements of Quadrant Two are already present in your unit?

Two Right–Image

Two Left–Inform

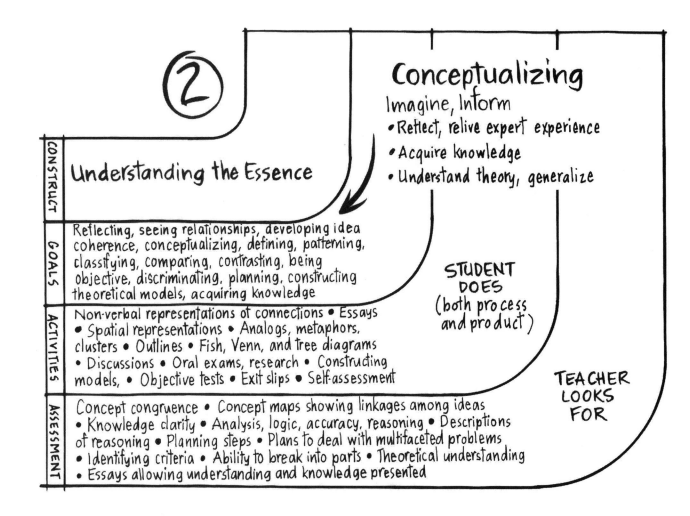

Conceptualizing

Imagine, Inform
- Reflect, relive expert experience
- Acquire knowledge
- Understand theory, generalize

CONSTRUCT

Understanding the Essence

GOALS

Reflecting, seeing relationships, developing idea coherence, conceptualizing, defining, patterning, classifying, comparing, contrasting, being objective, discriminating, planning, constructing theoretical models, acquiring knowledge

STUDENT DOES (both process and product)

ACTIVITIES

Non-verbal representations of connections • Essays • Spatial representations • Analogs, metaphors, clusters • Outlines • Fish, Venn, and tree diagrams • Discussions • Oral exams, research • Constructing models, • Objective tests • Exit slips • Self-assessment

TEACHER LOOKS FOR

ASSESSMENT

Concept congruence • Concept maps showing linkages among ideas • Knowledge clarity • Analysis, logic, accuracy, reasoning • Descriptions of reasoning • Planning steps • Plans to deal with multifaceted problems • Identifying criteria • Ability to break into parts • Theoretical understanding • Essays allowing understanding and knowledge presented

Step Two:
Enhancing the Quadrant Two, Right Mode Aspects of Your Lessons

Again, it's necessary to consider the right-mode and left-mode steps of Quadrant Two separately. The goals for Quadrant Two, Right Mode are:

Reflecting

Seeing relationships

Developing idea coherence

Patterning

In the exercise below, record some ideas for enhancing your own units in Quadrant Two, Right mode.

☆ **Quadrant Two, Right Mode Worksheet**

Bridging from Learner to Content

1. What is the unit's title?

2. What is the unit's concept?

3. What are the possible Bridges between the content and the concept?

4. How can students represent the bridge using another medium (pictures, music, drama, diagrams, creative writing – NOT essays or reports)?

5. How can this image lead to a big picture understanding for learners, one that connects the concept by placing it in a larger perspective? It should not be an arbitrary exercise, but one that draws the learners from their own subjective knowing into the expert information.

6. In this step, how can you get learners to reflect on what they already know – to see for themselves the connection between the content and Self?

7. Ask the art or music teachers for ideas. Record them here.

Enhancing the Quadrant Two, Left Mode Aspects of your Units

Here, we throw out a challenge to teachers. Do you know your content intimately? Are you completely fascinated with photosynthesis or Greek tragedy or 19th century poetry? If you are, we can practically guarantee that finding the concept and engaging learners in Quadrant One will come more easily.

The entire point of the first three steps of 4MAT is to show learners what is so amazing and fascinating about a subject. If you are not yourself fascinated, this will be a difficult task. And the material from the text or curriculum or standards will *not* contain this spark. That leaves it to you.

In Quadrant Two, you deliver the expert knowledge. Those experts were themselves fascinated with the material, but it may have lost some of its original enthusiasm. We urge you to find out what is fascinating about anything you teach. Bring in expert speakers, let learners interview experts in a field (a task made much easier using the Internet), uncover the arguments on both sides of controversies, etc.

Author Dennis note: Each day when I send my children to school I remind them that this could be the day they discover something that will change the direction of their lives, so they should pay attention. Of course they roll their eyes and groan, "Dad". Each day when I send them to school, I hope that their teacher will breathe life into the material that will help them recognize its wonder and fascination. As the primary liaison between content and learner, the teacher is the key.

1. What is the unit's title?

2. What is the unit's concept?

3. What is the bridge, the middle tier between your content and concept?

4. How might you encourage students to represent their understandings of your bridge nonverbally?

5. On a scale of 1-10, to what degree are you personally fascinated with this content? If this number is less than 5, seek outside help.

6. What external experts can you introduce that will offer a well-rounded presentation of expert knowledge? This may include: your personal expertise, text and media resources, web resources, current event resources, or live/technology-based interviews.

7. How will you engage learners in conversation during or following your presentation of the expert knowledge?

Some Lessons to Examine in Terms of "Twoness"

Examine the ways the following teachers designed their Quadrant Two activities. And note how they constructed their right- and left-mode activities. Discuss and possibly improve the Quadrant Two, Right and Left Mode activities in each of these lessons.

Here are some questions to consider before you begin:

How has the Right-mode step brought the learner's subjectivity into the picture? (The personal opinions/feelings learner's already have.)

How has the medium chosen enhanced understanding the content to follow?

How has the lecture been handled? Could it have been more demonstrative, visually, aurally, interactive?

Would that have helped or hindered the teacher's purpose?

Two steps of the following unit are described in detail: Quadrant Two, Right Mode and Quadrant Two, Left Mode. The activities in the other six steps are described in less detail as they are not necessary for our purpose. You are given enough information to know where the teacher hoped to go with her/his design in Quadrant Two.

☆ How might you and your small group improve the Quadrant Two of these lessons? Look at the scaling descriptions we use in Level Two Training. See what your group can add

Scaling Criteria
0 = suitable	1 = enriched	2 = Wow!

Quadrant Two Right Mode

0 The concept is transformed into an image using another medium besides words (prose).

+1 The image is moved to a metaview, one that connects the concept by placing it in a larger perspective.

+2 A conceptual "bridge" is created from direct experience to abstract concept. Learners are involved in reflective production, perhaps, visual, kinesthetic, or auditory experience that blends the emotional and the cognitive, yet remains very personal and subjective.

Quadrant Two Left Mode

0 Developmentally appropriate, organized information is transmitted that contains expert treatment of the concept.

+1 Same as above with the addition of appropriate video and/or guest expert.

+2 Interactive instruction (leading learners in transferable future directions) uses multiple methods including visuals and demonstrations, encourages diverse note-taking methods, e.g., mind-mapping, sketching as well as traditional means.

Middle School Social Studies

A 4MAT lesson plan

Concept: Life in the Middle Ages

Author: Sylvia Piper

Quadrant One, Right Mode

Objective: To provide students with an experience of the social levels of life in the Middle Ages.

Activity: The class is divided into a class system. Some students are vassals. Each of the vassals has four serfs and a working area with art supplies and mural paper. Their task is to depict life in the Middle Ages. Duties of the vassals: decide what goes on the mural, and which serf must do it. Duties of serfs: to do what the vassal tells them to do, and they must share profits of their labor with the vassals. (Snacks the teacher provides.)

Quadrant One, Left Mode

Objective: Analyze the vassal/serf relationship.

Activity: Students write their reactions and feelings and then share them with the class. After sharing their feelings they compile a list of insights gained from the experience. Teacher comes in and out of the discussion comparing the social and economic structure of our present-day world.

Quadrant Two, Right Mode

Objective: To integrate their Quadrant One experience with a feeling for daily life in the Middle Ages.

Activity: Teachers uses illustrations from *A Medieval Feast* by Aliki and excerpts from *The Story of King Arthur and His Knights* by Howard Pyle to introduce the basic organization of medieval society. In small groups students create a mindmap to reflect the basic organization of medieval society and how various lifestyles emerged. Teacher combines mindmaps from each group into one large mural for the whole class.

Assessment: How involved the students are and the quality of the mindmaps.

Quadrant Two, Left Mode

Objective: To teach the major concepts that created the Middle Ages.

Activity: Teacher present mini-lectures through film and video and music. Students read assignments. Concepts include: the feudal system, the culture of The Crusades, and agricultural development.

Assessment: Note taking quality, questions and interactions and teacher understanding checks.

Quadrant Three, Left Mode

Activity: Students maintain notebooks of readings and classroom interactions, and teacher and student-posed questions. Students choose one of the following activities to reinforce their learning: creating a crossword puzzle using the content which they exchange with other students, developing categories and creating answers for a jeopardy game to be played by the class, designing a class tapestry, creating a classroom timeline, writing a letter home describing your life as a page in the service of the king, writing a diary account of your day as lady of the manor.

Quadrant Three, Right Mode

Activity: In cooperative groups students expand their original mindmap to include everything they now know about life in the Middle Ages. Students begin preliminary investigations for a final project. They finalize these project ideas and submit a written contract to the teacher.

Quadrant Four, Left Mode

Activity: While working on their projects, the teams create a final exam and submit it to the teacher. Team exams are combined and the teacher creates the final.

Quadrant Four, Right Mode

Activity: Students present at a Medieval Faire which they plan and coordinate with all its pageantry: parade, performances, displays, costumes, art and music.

☆ Possible Ways to Improve this Lesson

A 4MAT lesson plan

High School English Literature

Concept: Choice, *A Man for All Seasons*

Author: Lynn Dieter

Quadrant One, Right Mode

Objective: To connect students to the idea of making choices: how we make choices, why we feel guilt, and how our values dictate our choices.

Activity: Students in groups play *Scruples* by Milton Bradley. Each group must reach consensus. Students then "talk-story" about a hard choice they have made, why it was difficult, and what part guilt played in the event.

Assessment: Intensity of the small group discussion.

Quadrant One, Left Mode

Objective: To formulate a concept of how choices are made and how we rank our values.

Activity: Students keep a diary for one weekend of choices they have made. They then prioritize these choices identifying their hardest choices and their subsequent actions. They share their choices creating a composite list. Teacher leads a discussion about the hard choices and the function of guilt, and how our values work in our lives. The issue of how choices are sometimes "gray" is discussed and put in the context of how we use our values to determine our actions in these murky situations.

Quadrant Two, Right Mode

Objective: To preface the reading of the drama by helping students see how we see ourselves.

Activity: Each student interviews five people with an eye to finding out how people view themselves. The class will read ahead in the play to the metaphor that More uses to describe himself, *"…it is an area no bigger than a tennis court."*

Students will create a metaphor to express that which is their tennis court, that part of them they create over time that they will not change for anyone. How often is that part involved in a choice?

Assessment: Sharing of the personal metaphors

Quadrant Two, Left Mode

Objective: To read and analyze the play with a focus on the choices made by the characters.

Activity: Students read the play, keeping track of places where More makes a choice. Lecture and discussions focus on the *"Common Man"* as an antagonist to More and the idea that *"No man is an island."*

Assessment: Students' notes, and a quiz of salient events in the play.

Quadrant Three, Left Mode

Activity: Students take each convention in the play, and trace its use through the drama. They show how Bolt's manipulation did or did not work in terms of his manipulation of characters. Students read Albert Speer's article asserting the Nazis were just following orders. They must relate his stance to the play and the notion of individual choices.

Quadrant Three, Right Mode

Activity: Students select one character and show how the outcome would have been different if another choice had been made. Class views Paul Scofield's portrayal of More, followed by a discussion of the metaphor for Self. Students create an epitaph for More's tomb. It must be metaphorical.

Quadrant Four, Left Mode

Activity: Students present a living example of someone who lost something by making a choice. The subject must be analyzed in terms of the guilt and sorrow and ability to live with the outcome of the choice. The analysis must be presented in theme form.

Quadrant Four, Right Mode

Activity: In triads, using pictures taken from print, students create collages to portray how our characters are built on the choices we make.

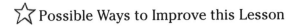 Possible Ways to Improve this Lesson

Chapter Five

4MAT in Action!
Doing Quadrant Three

Quadrant Three–The Tinkering and Ownership Begins

Quadrant Three goes from practice to tinkering,
from the way it is to the way it can be used.

From the known ideas, sequences, events and procedures to new insights, to streamlined sequences, to elegant short cuts, to patterns in events.

Quadrant Three is where the learning transfers.

Quadrant Three is getting it right so you can use it and adapt it in multiple ways.

The learner takes over somewhere in Quadrant Three.

The learner moves from Left Mode practicing to personal usefulness.

This is a big move.

It's where performance begins.

It's a great moment for a teacher when the student begins to take the lead.

The teacher becomes a coach and a cheerleader, a lighthouse keeper for excellence, while the student becomes the practitioner.

The Tension of Opposites: Quadrant Three and Quadrant One

Throughout the 4MAT Cycle, the tension of opposites drives the momentum of learning. Examine Quadrant Three in terms of Quadrant One.

Quadrant One answers the question **Why?** It helps learners and teachers see reasons.

Quadrant Three answers the question **How?** Now that I know *Why* I should know this, I need to discover *How* to use it to enhance my success in the world.

The Quadrant One, Left mode step uses the key word ATTEND. When you break this word down into its parts, you have TEND (stretch) and AD (towards).

The opposite Quadrant Three, Right Mode step, broken into parts is TEND (stretch) and EX (out of).

Quadrant One involves internalization. Quadrant Three involves externalization.

Quadrant One is "What it means to me." Quadrant Three is "What it means out in the world."

Quadrant One moves from feeling to reflection. Quadrant Three moves from concepts to action.

The Left Mode of Quadrant Three

Pure and simple the task is to know it the way the experts know it and to do it the way they do it.

The Right Mode of Quadrant Three

The Right Mode of Quadrant Three involves student adaptation, merging the expert knowledge, and expert procedures with the student's skill and personal capability.

A coming together of learning and learner.

Another point of celebration for the teacher.

4MAT in Action!

Doing Quadrant Three

Now consider your developing units in terms of Quadrant Three.

Step One
What's Already There?

It's likely that there are elements of Quadrant Three already in your units, particularly elements of Quadrant Three, Left Mode with worksheets, guided practice, etc. Throw them on the wheel! Do you have an experiment? Computer practice? "Learning Centers?"

Delineating between the left and right mode steps of Quadrant Three is fairly obvious. If an activity involves personal practice (even group practice with learners taking turns), it can be characterized as left mode.

If an activity involves interpretation, extension of concepts, making use of an idea, then it probably belongs in the right mode step. In Quadrant Three, students *begin* to transfer learning to life, they interpret, they use. Performance and integration follow.

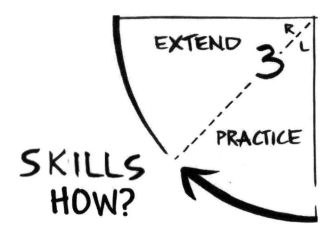

EXTEND

3 R
L

PRACTICE

SKILLS
HOW?

☆ Using the diagram, jot down those elements of your unit that seem to fit in Quadrant Three. Refer to the diagram for help with this alignment. What elements of Quadrant Three are already present in your unit?

Three Left–Practice

Three Right–Extend

Chapter Five: 4MAT in Action! Doing Quadrant Three

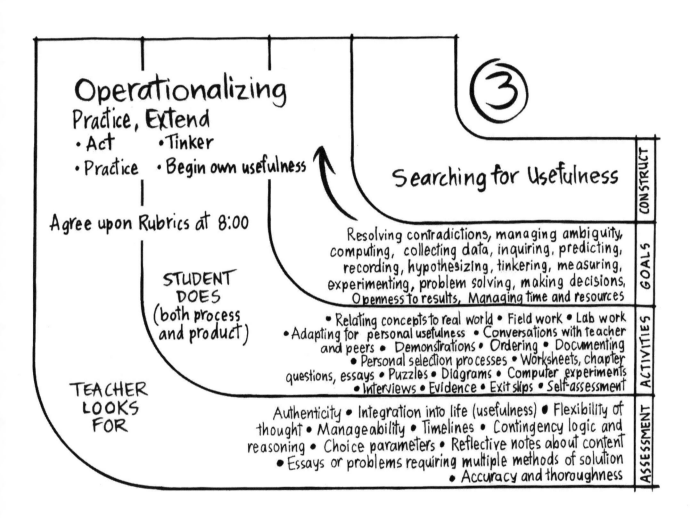

Operationalizing

Practice, Extend

- Act
- Practice
- Tinker
- Begin own usefulness

Agree upon Rubrics at 8:00

STUDENT DOES
(both process and product)

TEACHER LOOKS FOR

③

Searching for Usefulness

GOALS

Resolving contradictions, managing ambiguity, computing, collecting data, inquiring, predicting, recording, hypothesizing, tinkering, measuring, experimenting, problem solving, making decisions, Openness to results, Managing time and resources

ACTIVITIES

- Relating concepts to real world • Field work • Lab work • Adapting for personal usefulness • Conversations with teacher and peers • Demonstrations • Ordering • Documenting • Personal selection processes • Worksheets, chapter questions, essays • Puzzles • Diagrams • Computer experiments • Interviews • Evidence • Exit slips • Self-assessment

ASSESSMENT

Authenticity • Integration into life (usefulness) • Flexibility of thought • Manageability • Timelines • Contingency logic and reasoning • Choice parameters • Reflective notes about content • Essays or problems requiring multiple methods of solution • Accuracy and thoroughness

CONSTRUCT

Step Two
Enhance what's already there

Look at skills and transferability. First identify what skills will be involved and enhanced as content is mastered. Then identify the transferability of those skills. You will find that standards contain primarily knowledge and skills. (In fact the standards in Texas are actually called Texas Essential Knowledge and Skills!) It's up to the teacher to help learners transfer skills to life so knowledge is retained and useful beyond the state test.

For your 4MAT units, state the immediate personal value of the concept you identified for *all* students *now* (not in their future). In Quadrant One, you asked students to consider this value. In Quadrant Three, you must get them to *use* it.

You need to find the value of the material out in the learner's world.

It's helpful to revisit your Concept at this stage of the unit.

For example, in an Algebra unit, small groups can create a collage of real-world algebra uses, from tipping to human relations, and present their collection to the class.

☆ **Quadrant Three Worksheet**

What do I do with this stuff?

1. What is the title of the unit?

2. What is the unit's concept?

3. How is it used in the real world?

4. Can students go find instances of these real-world uses?

5. In what ways is this knowledge personally useful? Note: "They will need it later in life," or "They will need it if they become chemical engineers," are *not* appropriate responses.

6. How can you encourage students to provide for themselves the "evidence" of the material's usefulness?

7. How can you challenge students to demonstrate this usefulness in many different fields of endeavor? Remember the most important ideas are important "across the board."

8. The word interpret is defined as "to conceive the significance of". Its etymology is based on the notion of a "go-between". How can you challenge students to interpret this new material? How can they serve as the go-between from the world of abstract knowledge to the world of usefulness?

Chapter Five: 4MAT in Action! Doing Quadrant Three

127

Some Lessons to Examine in Terms of "Threeness"

Examine the ways the following teachers designed their Quadrant Three activities. And note how they constructed their right- and left-mode activities. Then discuss and possibly improve the Quadrant Three, Right and Left Mode activities in each of these lessons.

Here are some questions to consider before you begin:

How did the practice in the lesson equip students to adapt the learning?

How tedious was the practice or did the students see the usefulness of where they were headed?

Was the practice for school's sake, for the "test", or for the students' ultimate use of the learning in their own lives?

Could the students have created their own practice activities for each other?

Could out-of-the-classroom practice have been designed for more relevance?

The following steps are described in detail: Quadrant Three, Right Mode and Quadrant Three, Left Mode. The activities in the other six steps are described in less detail as they are not necessary for our purpose of examining Quadrant Three in depth. You are given enough information to know where the teacher hoped to go with her/his design in Quadrant Three.

☆ How might you and your small group improve the Quadrant Three of these lessons? Look at the scaling descriptions we use in Level Two Training. See what your group can add

Scaling Criteria

0 = suitable	1 = enriched	2 = Wow!

Quadrant Three Left Mode

0 Appropriate guided practice, i.e. workbook pages, teacher prepared exercises, etc.

+1 In addition, students use guided practice involving learning centers and using multiple modalities.

+2 Analysis of information now known by students is done individually or in groups. Students have an opportunity to look at information in a new way (compare, contrast, problem solve, etc.). In addition, students may create additional multi-modal practice activities and tests to be shared with peers.

Quadrant Three Right Mode

0 Personal "tinkering" is required in some way.

+1 Students have opportunities to design real problems with real-world application and agreed-upon rubrics.

+2 Multiple options for tinkering are available which take into account learning styles, hemisphericity, and modality preferences of learners.

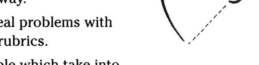

High School United States History

Concept: The American Revolution

Authors: Neil Robinson and Linda Aird Vretos

A 4MAT lesson plan

Quadrant One, Right Mode

Objective: To create an experience of revolution for the students.

Activity: Students are presented with two decrees from the school administration. Students must pay a tax on all denim material. Students may not wear Reebok, Adidas, or Nike apparel. Students may not wear any Limited or Gap apparel. There is no appeal to this directive by order of the School Board. The teacher presents this in a serious manner with a seemingly logical rationale for these new rules.

Quadrant One, Left Mode

Objective: To enhance student ability to experience the violation of their rights.

Activity: Teacher-led discussion analyzing reactions to the new directives. Small groups are then formed and students discuss and then list the kinds of nonviolent protest they could organize to change the new rules. At the end of this exercise the students are told the new directives do not exist. Students will voice their reactions. The teacher will lead a whole class discussion of how people feel when they believe their rights are being violated.

Quadrant Two, Right Mode

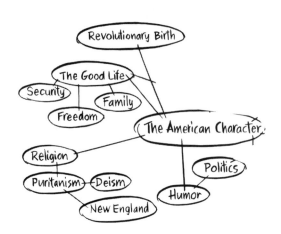

Objective: To create an understanding of the diversity of American society in the years leading up to the Revolutionary War in order to understand how the grievances they had against the King of England helped form them into a "people".

Activity: Teacher introduces music and artwork from that time. Students form into groups and each group also reads a different set of letters and diaries written by real people. The groups' task is to create a picture of the diversity of the colonists and to create a large mindmap to share with the other groups regarding their insights.

Quadrant Two, Left Mode

Objective: To give information and clarity as to the events preceding the Revolutionary War.

Activity: Teacher lectures on significant events, and assigns readings, videos and Internet sites.

Quadrant Three, Left Mode

Objective: To enhance the students' understanding of the actions of the English king and Parliament and how it affected the colonists.

Activity: Students complete a data retrieval sheet listing the dates of certain Parliament actions, and their economic impacts, including social impacts and political impacts. Teacher supplies materials to assist the students in this task.

Assessment: Completion of data retrieval sheets.

Quadrant Three, Right Mode

Objective: To extend their insights into the minds and heart of the colonists.

Activity: Small groups become "Committees of Correspondence". Based on research given by the teacher, each Committee reacts to two grievances, and creates a letter to Parliament describing their feelings, and the actions they may be forced to take. Each student also creates a diary entry as to their feelings and fears about the consequence of their actions.

Assessment: The quality of the letters and the diary entries using an agreed upon rubric.

Quadrant Four, Left Mode

Objective: To edit, critique and refine their work.

Activity: Each team presents a first draft of its letter of grievance to one other group for ideas and reactions as well as to the teacher for a final go-ahead.

Quadrant Four, Right Mode

Objective: To perform what has been learned.

Activity: Student committees present their final projects. They do so in skits adding music, art and diary entries from the original colonists as well as their own. Each student must make an entry regarding their insights into any understanding they now have regarding failed negotiations and how this may lead to more serious actions.

☆ Possible Ways to Improve this Lesson

A 4MAT lesson plan

High School United States History

Concept: Economic change and the Civil Right Movement

Author: Betty Holland, 11th–12th grade teacher, McAdory High School, Birmingham, Alabama

Quadrant One, Right Mode

Objectives: To visually experience life as a minority living in the South before the 1960's.

Activity: A trip to the Civil Rights Institute for a video presentation and the "Barriers Gallery", a visual experience of what daily economic life was like for minorities pre-Civil Rights. Students will also spend time in the computerized database at the Institute as a prelude to a research project further on in the unit.

Assessment: Level of student interest and participation.

Quadrant One, Left Mode

Objective: That students enhance their ability to reach a consensus about the most appropriate actions to take regarding misstatements of income.

Activity: Class discussion of reactions regarding the differences between minorities and whites during this time period. Students make journal entries.

Assessment: Level of participation and journal entry reflection.

Quadrant Two, Right Mode

Objective: Students will be able to illustrate the material under study and recreate the timeline of economic changes through the medium of advertising.

Activity: Using magazines, Internet, library reference materials, the "Time Almanac" CD, students find advertising illustrating the roles of minorities before the Civil Rights legislation of the 1960's.

Assessment: Quality of the compilation of images and accuracy of the pieces chosen.

Quadrant Two, Left Mode

Objective: To learn the key information on the Civil Rights Movement and the 1960's legislation, with particular emphasis on economic changes made possible by the legislation.

Activity: Teacher lecture with interactive clarification questioning.

Assessment: Student participation and student notes, and teacher-created test of important information.

Quadrant Three: Left Mode

Objective: To begin gathering the research needed to create a comparison of advertising before and after the Civil Rights Legislation.

Activity: Students work in small groups and use all available research sources.

Assessment: Pertinence of data gathered.

Quadrant Three: Right Mode

Objective: To compare and contrast the economic positives before and after the 1960's legislation and to reflect and comment on the work still to be done.

Activity: Using all the connected data, images etc. students working in their small groups will create timeline displays in three dimensions on the changing economic roles of minorities since 1960.

Assessment: A pre-agreed upon rubric—accuracy, choice of objects, originality, and artistry.

Quadrant Four, Left Mode

Objective: To refine their exhibits.

Activity: Small groups visit the first drafts and plans of all other groups and write suggestions for improvement.

Assessment: Quality of the suggestions and the spirit in which they are given.

Quadrant Four, Right Mode

Objective: To display the work of the small groups for a larger audience.

Activity: Students enhance their exhibits using the suggestions they choose. The work of the student groups is displayed in a central location and a special presentation scheduled for an audience chosen from the community. Each group will give a verbal explanation of their thinking regarding their design and their reflections on what they have learned as well as what they feel still needs to be done.

☆ Possible Ways to Improve this Lesson

Chapter Six

Perfecting Your Performance: Quadrant Four

Quadrant Four is Doing It All

If you did Quadrant One well you motivated your students and led them to see the value in the material you were about to teach. You engaged the Self in your students.

That engagement went with them into Quadrant Two, where you helped them to conceptualize, to learn from the experts what they had come to value in Quadrant One.

When you were working in Quadrant Two, you were doing both Quadrants One and Two at once.

You had the students with you as you gave them details and helped them explore ideas and insights, facts and findings.

When they went on to Quadrant Three to practice and master the skills that accompanied the material, then the Self and the Content and the Skills, all three quadrants, came together—bringing the students to expertise.

Then in Quadrant Four, you combined it all.

Value, Content, Skill and Performance simultaneously.

Performance, the Hallmark of Quadrant Four

An important caution, the performance must become part of their lives. Whatever you create in Quadrant Four must lead students to use the learning in some adaptive way in their own places and in their own time.

If Quadrant Four is the culmination of a successful learning experience, it becomes a beginning, a new way of feeling, reflecting, thinking, doing, and even being.

When you are working in Quadrant Four, you are doing it all.

The Tension of Opposites: Quadrant Four and Quadrant Two

Throughout the 4MAT Cycle, the tension of opposites drives the momentum of learning. Looking at Quadrant Four in terms of Quadrant Two can be instructive.

Quadrant Two answers the question **What?** It adds the voices of the experts. Quadrant Four answers the question **If?** It merges the voices of the experts with the individual learner.

The Quadrant Two, Left-mode step uses the key word INFORM. When you break this word down into its parts, you have FORM (to add shape or form) and IN (into).

The opposite Quadrant Four, Right-Mode step, broken into parts is FORM (add shape or form) and PER (through). Imagine a learning that enters into your body and then flows back out of you, both learner and learning changed by the process.

Quadrant Two involves what the authors think about it. Quadrant Four involves how my life is enhanced by it.

Quadrant Two moves from reflection to concepts. Quadrant Four moves from action back full circle to (newly informed) experience.

The Left Mode of Quadrant Four

The Left Mode of Quadrant Four is to polish, to insure that students refine their work.

> Re-fine—re: to turn back; finis: end, to purify, to remove unsuitable characteristics, to use precision and subtlety of thought, to polish, to make excellent.

This is an important step for the obvious reason that polishing takes time and effort, and results in an improved product.

A less obvious reason is that students need to understand how to become their own best critics, how to add discipline to their doings in the world.

The Right Mode of Quadrant Four

The Right-Mode final step is difficult to really label "right mode" because the integration of learning that is taking place brings all systems into play. Learning is integrated into performance.

Simultaneity, planning, sequence, tone, impact on listeners/readers, visual representations, audio embellishments, timing, and personal presence. **Major whole-brained stuff.**

When learners are performing they are using the entire brain-mind system.

4MAT in Action!

Doing Quadrant Four

Now consider your developing units in terms of Quadrant Four.

Step One
What's Already There?

It's likely that there are elements of Quadrant Four already in your units. Throw them on the wheel! If an activity involves performance, creative expressions of understanding, originality, exhibits, new understandings, synthesis of ideas, publications, or presentations then it's a good candidate for Quadrant Four.

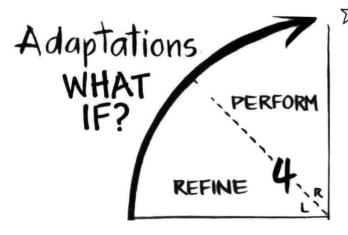

☆ Using the diagram, jot down those elements of your unit that seem to fit in Quadrant Four. Refer to the diagram for help with this alignment. What elements of Quadrant Four are already present in your unit?

Four Left–Refine

Four Right–Perform

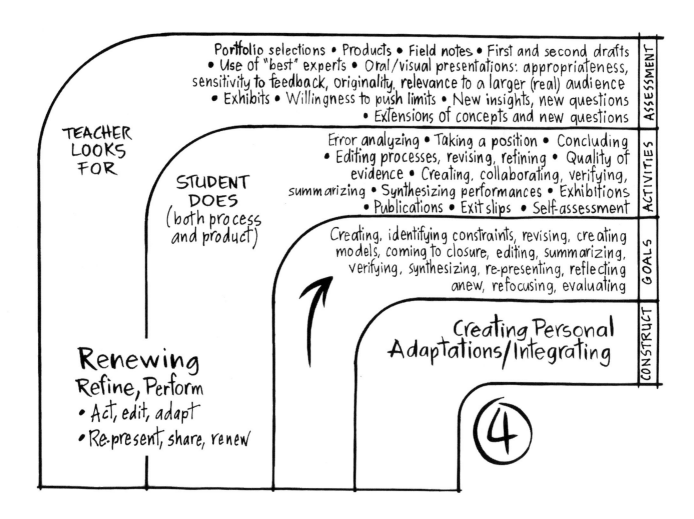

TEACHER
LOOKS
FOR

ASSESSMENT

Portfolio selections • Products • Field notes • First and second drafts • Use of "best" experts • Oral/visual presentations: appropriateness, sensitivity to feedback, originality, relevance to a larger (real) audience • Exhibits • Willingness to push limits • New insights, new questions • Extensions of concepts and new questions

STUDENT
DOES
(both process
and product)

ACTIVITIES

Error analyzing • Taking a position • Concluding • Editing processes, revising, refining • Quality of evidence • Creating, collaborating, verifying, summarizing • Synthesizing performances • Exhibitions • Publications • Exit slips • Self-assessment

GOALS

Creating, identifying constraints, revising, creating models, coming to closure, editing, summarizing, verifying, synthesizing, re-presenting, reflecting anew, refocusing, evaluating

CONSTRUCT

Creating Personal
Adaptations/Integrating

④

Renewing
Refine, Perform
• Act, edit, adapt
• Re-present, share, renew

Step Two
How can you enhance what's there?

Quadrant Four is the integration of learning. To summarize the last half of the cycle, consider this example from music.

In Quadrant Two Left Mode (INFORM), the musician memorizes the music, the expert knowledge.

In Quadrant Three, Left Mode (PRACTICE) she practices it, separating it from the mechanics so she can express herself fully in later steps.

In Quadrant Three, Right Mode (EXTEND) she no longer needs to worry about notes and mechanics. She can focus fully on the task of interpretation, stretching the expert knowledge based on her understandings and unique identity, acting as go-between from knowledge to the physical world.

In Quadrant Four, Left Mode (REFINE), she compares her interpretations with the music as originally written, stepping back, analyzing, making sure interpretations did not stray too far.

Finally, in Quadrant Four, Right Mode (PERFORM), the new material is "formed through". She has integrated it with herself. Both learner and learning have merged to create a new thing in the world.

Quadrant Four represents a culmination of learning, a creative manifestation of material learned. This often takes the form of a re-teach or a performance of some kind. Technology can be used very effectively in the latter part of the 4MAT cycle where product is emphasized. The many forms of authoring that technology offers are ideal activities for Quadrants Three and Four.

 **☆ Quadrant Four Worksheet**

Me + It = Something New!

1. What is the unit's title?

2. What is the concept?

3. In what ways do students express understanding of the material?

4. Using what you know about right and left mode types of assessments, would you characterize the assessments for this unit as primarily right or left mode? Essays, facts recall and worksheets go into the left mode column and creative assignments go in the right mode column.

5. If your answers to the above is primarily left, what can you add to the conclusion of this unit that will allow learners to creatively express their new understandings? What can they author or publish? (Consider the many ways to publish these days: PowerPoint, web page building, iMovie, creative writing, multimedia, etc. Remember to return to the concept as you consider this question.)

6. In what ways can students take the content in new directions, create new questions, advance the body of knowledge?

Some Lessons to Examine in Terms of "Fourness"

Examine the ways these teachers designed their Quadrant Four activities.

Note how they constructed their right- and left-mode activities.

Here are some questions to consider before you begin:

> Was the refinement process organized so the students helped each other?
>
> Did the students get to confer with the teacher before their final task?
>
> How did the required performance encompass the usefulness of the lesson?
>
> What kind of sharing was involved?
>
> What kind of celebratory activity happened?
>
> Could there have been more?
>
> How many elements in the final requirement had ramifications for the students' lives outside of school?

The two steps of Quadrant Four are described in detail. The activities in the other six steps are presented with less detail as they are not necessary for our purpose. You are given enough information to know where the teacher hoped to go with her/his design in Quadrant Four.

☆ How might you and your small group improve the Quadrant Four of these lessons? Look at the scaling descriptions we use in Level Two Training. See what your group can add.

Scaling Criteria

0 = suitable	1 = enriched	2 = Wow!

Quadrant Four Left Mode

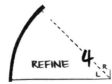

0 Teacher and students evaluate learning applications for relevance and originality.

+1 Students edit, refine, rework, analyze their own effectiveness.

+2 Facilitates students in "going the extra mile" (input from teacher and peers) to improve their meaningful application of the concept before sharing.

Quadrant Three Right Mode

0 Students report/demonstrate what they have learned.

+1 Learning is enjoyed and celebrated.

+2 Learners integrate, (through some refocusing application, public when possible) and new learning happens. Most students experience strong emotional involvement.

A 4MAT lesson plan

High School Art

Concept: The Parts and The Whole

Author: Renee Shamosh

Quadrant One, Right Mode

Objective: To raise student awareness enhanced through experiencing the gradual revelation from parts to whole.

Activity: Hand out a different child's puzzle piece to each student in a small group.

Question: What if anything comes to mind when you see this piece?

Answer: I do not see anything.

Hand out a second piece.

Question: Now what do you see?

Answer: I still do not see any connection.

Hand out remaining pieces and puzzle forms into Humpty Dumpty.

Reaction: Oh, wow, now I see it.

Follow up with a discussion of seeing parts and seeing wholes.

Quadrant One, Left Mode

Objective: To become familiar with an artist who struggled with the issue of wholes and parts.

Activity: Read and share some of the photos and writings about artist Chuck Close and his work. Talk about the difficulties he faced in trying to learn from whole to part and his success when he moved to working from part to whole. Chuck Close was told to forget about higher education. Instead, he found an open enrollment junior college where he took art classes. He went on to a distinguished career in art against incredible odds, both caused by

Art and music become more and more important tools to enrich lessons around the 4MAT framework. Are you stuck for a great Quadrant Two, Right Mode step? Try asking the art or music teacher. You'll be amazed at what they can offer. Art should NOT be relegated to special classes that take place all too infrequently. The Arts can and should be integrated into the regular classroom regularly!

his approach to learning, considered a disability, as well as physical and emotional obstacles.

"I'm overwhelmed by the whole, but by breaking images into small units, I make each decision a bite-sized decision."

Today, as one of the most admired artists in the world, if you step close to his canvas, and you see hundreds of little abstract paintings. Only from a distant does the actual face emerge. (Greenberg and Jordan, *Chuck Close Up Close*, 1998)

Quadrant Two, Right Mode

Objective: To have students experience how parts fit into wholes and gain insight into the process.

Activity: Students in their groups are given pieces of a face cut into squares, one face per group. They reassemble the face puzzle.

Quadrant Two, Left Mode

Objective: That students will review their understanding of value in art as a prelim to their final assignment.

Activity: Previous lessons relating to value are reviewed. Examples include:

A. Pencil value scale, learning to create a full range of 8-10 values from white to black in pencil.

B. Still life object shaded in pencil using the value scale as a guide. Objects should reflect the full range of values that are represented in the value scale.

C. Still life composition using white chalk on black paper. The full range of values should be used with shades of white chalk and the black of the paper.

Quadrant Three, Left Mode

Objective: That students improve their ability to work with enlargements and values.

Activity: Each student enlarges a one-inch box into a twelve-inch box focusing only on value. Each student group reassembles twelve-inch boxes to create drawn images of value.

Quadrant Three, Right Mode

Objectives: That students use their knowledge and skill with value in an original way. That students will prove their understanding of quality by creating a rubric to measure degrees of excellence.

Activity: Create a variety of patterns that reflect value, give choice-pencil or ink or paint. Create a rubric for evaluating what would be an A, a B or a C project. Create a monochromatic value scale.

Quadrant Four, Left Mode

Objectives: That students will create an original work. That students will exercise the proper skills in critiquing one another's work.

Activity: Create an image of textures using your textured values. Create a monochromatic self-portrait. Group critiques individual works.

Assessment: Using an agreed-upon rubric students share and critique each other's work.

Quadrant Four, Right Mode

Objective: To have students enhance their ability to display art and to manage an art show.

Student art is displayed in the high school gallery show. (Yonkers, New York). Parents, students, staff and community members are invited to attend. This show is held in conjunction with the annual National Art Honor Society Induction ceremony. Student discussions about how each project helps to make a whole art form. This could spark further discussion of where else this technique (parts to whole) can be useful in other learning activities.

NOTE: *Some of the artwork samples that accompany this lesson are available on our website. Also note that this lesson will be available on our web site, via 4MATION LiveText® at http://4mat.livetext.com/doc/68904, including the pictures. It has been made "public" so anyone can view it.*

☆ Possible Ways to Improve this Lesson

Middle School Math

A 4MAT lesson plan

Concept: Measures of Central Tendency

Author: Robert Bates

Quadrant One, Right Mode

Objective: That student will connect "fairness" with "average" or "making things even".

Activity: Students are asked to determine the average number of chips in chocolate chip cookies. When students suggest counting the chips, teacher distributes unequal piles of cookies to pairs of students with the condition that they may be eaten only when the task is completed. Students who are short-changed will request either more cookies or a redistribution. The piles are then made more even and then the original activity continues.

Quadrant One, Left Mode

Objective: That students are able to list situations in their lives in which students needed to "level" things out. To enhance student's ability to find an average.

Activity: Teachers asks: Why do you feel better, or worse, about the redistribution of the cookies? What else could have been done? What was a situation in your own life where you had to make things even?

Quadrant Two, Right Mode

Objective: To give students more ability to draw analogies to add to their skill in understanding and using averages.

Activity: Recall the story of *Goldilocks and the Three Bears*. How is Baby Bear's porridge like the cookie stacks? How is the porridge different from the cookie stacks? How could all of the porridge be made just right? Draw a picture (no words allowed) of "average".

Quadrant Two, Left Mode

Objective: That students will enhance their ability to differentiate between Mean, Median (the middle number) Mode (the most frequent number) and the Range, and to be able to determine each from a histogram.

Activity: Using the overhead projector the teacher demonstrates the concepts. A histogram is shown with the salaries of twelve employees from a made-up company. The four concepts are determined and identified specifically using this histogram. The students complete a short quiz using another set of data.

Quadrant Three, Left Mode

Objective: That students will learn to collect data, create a histogram and determine which measures of central tendency to use in finding an average.

Activity: 1.) Heights of all seventh graders and all eighth graders are determined. Students put the information on a histogram and the measures of central tendency are found. 2.) Students are then given a list of fictitious students and their weekly allowances. They work in groups to find Mean, Median, Mode and Range. The list should contain a fairly large range. The students must decide which measure to use to persuade their parents that they may need a raise in their allowances.

Quadrant Three, Right Mode

Objective: That students will design a project that shows the use or misuse of averages.

Activity: Students choose and do individual and /or group projects. Possible project choices: show how sport statistics can be enlightening or misleading, create a new Goldilocks story where "just right" is different, make a chart of the typical seventh grader, design a "just right" person, survey two grade levels above 7th grade and two below and come with the average allowances those students get.

Quadrant Four, Left Mode

Objective: That students will hand in a first draft of their project

Activity: Students help assess and critique each others' project drafts.

Assessment: Students present clear, concise descriptions of their projects and their use of averages with readable and visually pleasing visual plans.

Quadrant Four, Right Mode

Objective: That students will name their projects and complete them.

Activity: Sample titles are discussed and the projects are presented.

Assessment: The presentations are judged by an agreed-upon rubric that the students and the teacher create together. Information on the use and/or misuse of averages must be presented.

☆ Possible Ways to Improve this Lesson

A 4MAT lesson plan

High School English

Concept: Perspective, Thorton Wilder's *Our Town*

Author: Lori Barnett.

An examination of the contrast between the individual and the universal using *Our Town*, the context of the students' lives and the culture of their present time.

Quadrant One, Right Mode

Students create a journal of the small, seemingly insignificant things in their lives that make them smile. Students share their lists in small groups.

Quadrant One, Left Mode

Students classify their lists under four headings: house, family, town, and nature. Classifications are reported in the large group.

Quadrant Two, Right Mode

Students choose a day in their lives to relive and then create a visual representation that is divided into two sections: one showing the original day, and the second showing the "relived" day. (The teacher has modeled this reliving first and given them help in articulating the difference between these two states of knowing, the original and the life-experience enhancement of the memory.)

Quadrant Two, Left Mode

Students read the play and watch in-class presentation of key scenes. Students discuss the key themes: small-town life, and the differences in perspective between the living and the dead as presented in the play. Students discuss the role of the stage manager as a character representing multiple states of knowing, or multiple perspectives.

Quadrant Three, Left Mode

Students compile lists of contrasts in perspective and other conflicts in the play.

Quadrant Three, Right Mode

Students reread the stage manager's speech in which he describes the time capsule Grovers Corners (the town in the play) buried in the cornerstone of the bank. Then students create individual mini-capsules which they hide for a period of time, and then they create a large time capsule which typifies life in Ridgewood, New Jersey where this lesson was written and taught. They include music, literature, art, photos etc.

Quadrant Four, Left Mode

Students evaluate the time-capsule selections and make final choices, Then they create a ceremony, invitations to parents, appropriate burial site with official permission etc.

Quadrant Four, Right Mode

Students conduct the ceremony and invite guests for the unearthing in 25 years.

☆ Possible Ways to Improve this Lesson

Chapter Seven

Other Ways to Look at the Quadrants

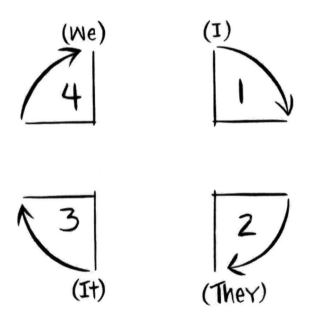

Try looking at the four quadrants from another perspective.

Think about Quadrant One as the place for "I". The activities you create as a teacher will all tend to impact on the "I" of your students, that is their own personal place.

☆ How might you create strategies in each part of the cycle looking at it from this perspective?

My "**I**" activities in Quadrant One

My "**They**" activities in Quadrant Two

My "**It**" activities in Quadrant Three

My "**We**" activities in Quadrant Four

The "I" of Quadrant One

Something is happening to the person's feelings. The teacher has connected the activity that is happening to the students' past experiences. Responses are:

"I know how that feels," or "I have been there myself."

The focus is not on the teacher, the focus is on the student connecting, the student remembering, the student resonating. It is not a telling time, it is a feeling, dialogue (sharing) time. And it is "**I**" all the way.

Oftentimes the teacher can even add to the discussion after it gets going and model the "**I**" part of her/his past experiences along with the students, as long as it does not take away from the student dialogue.

Chapter Seven: Other Ways to Look at the Quadrants

The "They" of Quadrant Two:

The experts are the **"They"**, the data is also, the facts and information, all **"They"**.

This is the listening time and the clearer the expert knowledge is, the more it is fashioned to suit the backgrounds and levels of the students, the better it is received.

Master teachers make sure all the students get it. They tell it in multiple ways, they have it available in some form to be checked after the fact for those who need to return to it in their own time, and they use visual as well as verbal forms to aid understanding.

The "It" of Quadrant Three

The "**It**" is concrete, it is something to have in the hand, meaning it is something one must do. It is other than the student, it is an object to be mastered, to be done, to be experimented with, to be practiced.

Practice needs to be multiple also. But most of all, practice needs to be structured. The students must follow a series of steps that lead them to fluid expertise so at some future point they will be able to discard the steps.

The teacher's goal is to lead students to personal expertise that is useful to them for the rest of their lives.

(How does memorizing the 50 state capitals of the United States fit into this definition of learning?)

The "We" of Quadrant Four

The purpose of Quadrant Four is to have students adapt learning to their world, and to use it to influence their future. So the emphasis here is on the **"We"** because the student is extending himself empowered with new learning out into a wider dialogue. Now the student has a more powerful voice.

☆ Try this perspective with one of your lessons. Put it on this wheel and then examine it for **I**, **They**, **It** and **We**.

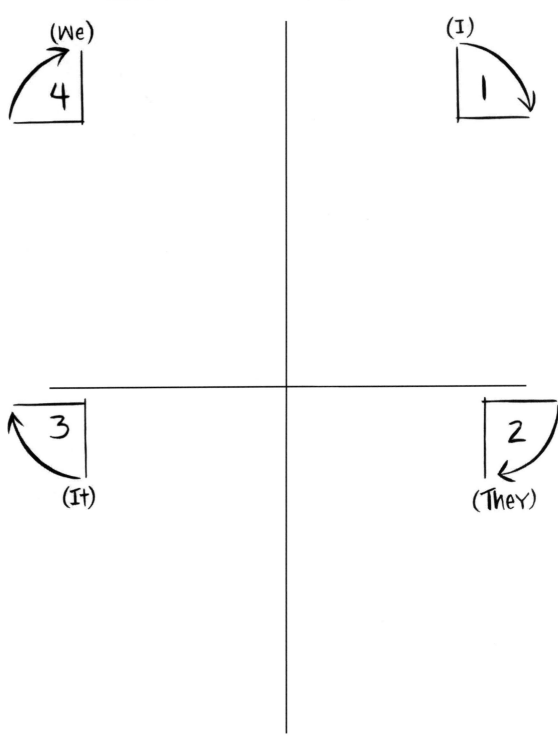

Chapter Seven: Other Ways to Look at the Quadrants

Yet Another Way to Look at the Quadrants

Try the inside/outside perspective.

Quadrants One and Two are inside—known from within.

Quadrants Three and Four are outside—known from without.

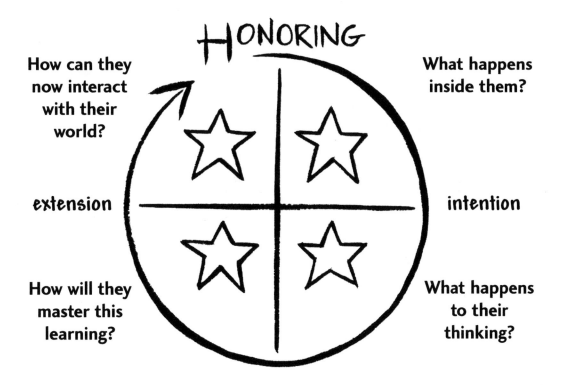

Looking at the Outside   **Looking at the Inside**

Discovering my
new power or lack of it

My perception

Interacting with the world

How it shakes out
with others

Speaking in my
own voice extended

Discovering my reactions

Learning from my doing

Reliving my experiences

Finding new questions

Hearing my inner voice

Learning how others do it

Data

Learning it their way

Knowledge

Seeing what happens to it

Expert views

Examining the reactions

Enhancing or critiquing
my beliefs

Becoming skilled with it

☆ Ask yourself these questions regarding one of your own lessons.

How can they now interact with their world?

What happens inside them?

How will they master this learning?

What happens to their thinking?

Chapter Eight

4MAT and Assessment

The following pages contain help in how to construct an assessment package for 4MAT units and plans. This chapter is divided into two distinct sections. First we look at assessing learners, then we look at assessing instruction.

Part One
Assessing Learners: It's about voice

The Voice Wheel describes how the 4MAT Cycle begins with dialogue, then moves to quiet listening and then finally leads students to speak in their own voices.

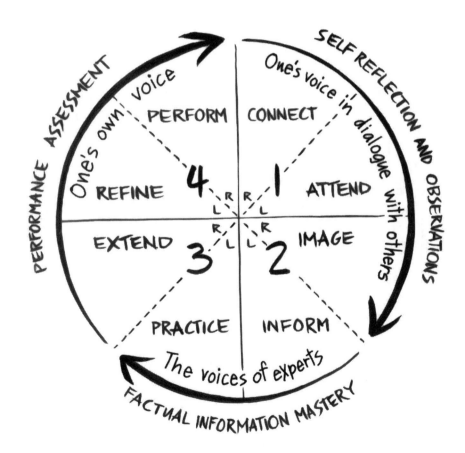

VOICES AROUND THE CYCLE

In the first three steps of 4MAT (Quadrant One and Quadrant Two, Right Mode) the students share their perceptions with one another. This is where students listen to the voices of others as well as to their own voice.

Think of a time when you were troubled about some issue and in the presence of a warm, listening friend, you were able to hear your own voice in a new way with insights that seemed to come to you suddenly. Such is the dialogue of **Quadrant One**.

The experience students share in the **Quadrant One, Right Mode** activity is designed to lead to that kind of sharing and insightfulness.

The nonverbal expression that is created in **Quadrant Two** will then reflect, not only the student's own perceptions of the concept, but a broader notion tempered/ validated/added to by the perceptions of fellow students.

In **Quadrant Two, Left Mode** and **Quadrant Three Left Mode**, the students listen to and read about the expert voices. This listening and absorbing time needs a different kind of assessment.

Then, at the dividing line in Quadrant Three the learner begins to take over the responsibility for learning. The goal is for students to speak in their own voices, combining the insights of their peers and the experts with their own voice. This is an exciting outcome of fine teaching.

VOICES AROUND THE CYCLE

One's own voice
Self Reflection and Observations
One's voice in dialogue with others
PERFORM | CONNECT
Performance Assessment
REFINE | 4 | 1 | ATTEND
EXTEND | 3 | 2 | IMAGE
PRACTICE | INFORM
The voices of experts
Factual Information Mastery

Note the differences in the assessment possibilities at each of the five places on the cycle where we suggest you consider assessments. These are described in more detail in the following pages.

☆ Discuss with your small group the three aspects of "**Voice**" that appear on the 4MAT Assessment Wheel:

"My voice in dialogue with others"

"The voices of the experts"

"In my own voice"

☆ Talk about how these three impact learning. Are some of them not honored in our schools? Which ones are left out? How does 4MAT bring in all three? Should all three be part of classroom teaching?

Looking at Your Techniques

Look at your assessment techniques in light of the following activities. Are you asking students to do mostly Quadrant Two and Three tasks?

While many of these tasks continue on around the cycle, it is helpful to understand the different kinds of thinking you are asking of learners when you think of learning as encompassing all four dimensions of the 4MAT Cycle: **meaning**, **ideas**, **skills** and **adaptations**.

Quadrant One: Meaning	Quadrant Two: Ideas	Quadrant Three: Skills	Quadrant Four: Adaptations
Connecting	Becoming informed	Practicing	Merging
Experiencing	Defining	Using	Creating
Collaborating	Understanding	Embellishing	Re-presenting
Discussing	Explaining	Synthesizing	Adapting
Assuming roles	Identifying	Locating	Developing
Relating to personally	Analyzing	Measuring	Illustrating-verbally
"Journaling"	Categorizing	Experimenting	Illustrating-nonverbally
Brainstorming	Imaging & patterning	Tinkering and editing	Exploring
Imagining	Sequencing	Interpreting	Expanding
Hunching	Knowing	Reconstructing	Performing
Sharing	Relating to other concepts	Debating	Polishing
Empathizing	Recognizing	Commenting	Sharing
Responding	Picturing	Paraphrasing	Elaborating
Listening	Listing	Arranging in chronological order	Synthesizing
Questioning	Classifying	Comparing	Extending
			Making
			Questioning anew

Assessment Continuum

Look at "On The Way"

Look at "At The Gate"

What balance do you think exists between these two modes of assessment in the average American school?

What balance exists in your classroom?

To Sum   **"On the Way"**

To Form   **"At the Gate"**

Summative Assessment (At the Gate)	**Formative Assessment (On the Way)**
To measure what was done	To perfect a process
Method is measurement	Method is description
Quantitative	Qualitative
Did we do what we wanted to do?	Ongoing reaction to treatment with an eye to developing it
Data for reporting, decisions, checking up on what's learned (which can lead to goal-setting for the next time)	Data for growth and change, checkpoints for adaptations (goal-setting while you are doing it)
What was learned?	Where are you in the learning of this?
Completion oriented	Developmental
At certain times–a snapshot	Ongoing–a video
"ed"–What happened	"ing"–How are we doing

☆ Do this exercise with a partner.

Review the following list of assessment tools. Classify each as favoring either "On The Way" or "At The Gate".

Give your rationale.

At The Gate	On The Way
Critical exit performance places	Assessing progress

a demonstration

a journal

an essay

a term paper

a standardized test

a diorama

a poster

a student-created skit

a mindmap

a group discussion

a quiz

a worksheet

analogs

an outline

a 3-dimensional model

a unit test

a graph

an oral presentation

a puppet show

field notes

a metaphor

an interview report

Rubrics

Rubric: a scoring system that describes exemplary, competent and not yet criteria.

Give your students exemplary examples of what you want. (For example, an English teacher with a sophomore class makes A+ essays from the senior class available to her students.) Also help them create their own rubrics. Rubrics need to be developed by the teacher and with the students. They need to be clear and available to both students and parents.

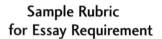

Sample Rubric
for Essay Requirement

EXEMPLARY

1. Coherence–the organization of the content is very clear and the ideas flow together.
2. Memorability—the writer entices the reader to read on and the treatment of the material leaves a lasting impression.
3. Persuasiveness—the writing makes a major appeal to believability. There is support for the ideas, analysis is provided with relevant and concrete examples.
4. Style and Mechanics—there is a clear, unique style. There are almost no errors in usage, grammar, or mechanics.

COMPETENT

1. Coherence–the organization of the content is not always clear but most of the ideas flow together.
2. Memorability—the writer entices the reader to read on, but the enticement is spooky, there are places where the reader's interest wanes. The treatment of the material, while adequate does not impact in a lasting way.
3. Persuasiveness—the writing makes a suitable appeal to believability. There is support for the ideas, some analysis is provided with relevant and concrete examples, although more concise examples would help.
4. Style and Mechanics—there is a style to the writing, although not sustained throughout the piece. There are a few errors in usage, grammar, or mechanics.

INCOMPLETE

Writing is deficient in two or more of the criteria.

Adapted from Grant Wiggins, Assessing Student Performance: Exploring the Purpose and Limits of Testing.
www.grantwiggins.org

☆ Try the following in your small group or by yourself as an experience in the rubrics process. Create a rubric for a first grade puppet show. Score A for exemplary, B for Good and C for suitable. D and F are not acceptable. The first one has been done for you. Come up with two additional criteria and rubrics.

Criteria: Something that must be there, the most essential qualities. Do the criteria enable you to discriminate between exemplary and competent?

Puppet Show (Grade 1) Criteria 1 Student creation of the puppets	Exemplary	Competent	Not Yet
Student creation of the puppets	Masterful in creation and characterization of the puppets: originality in personalizing, authentic interaction between puppet characters.	Each puppet has a costume and a characterization that is appropriate to its role in the show.	The puppets are not very appealing. Their costumes or characterizations are not especially suited to their roles.

Puppet Show (Grade 1) Criteria 2	Exemplary	Competent	Not Yet

Puppet Show (Grade 1) Criteria 3	Exemplary	Competent	Not Yet

The Places for Assessment on the 4MAT Wheel

It is important that students bring a certain ragamuffin barefoot irreverence to their studies;
they are not here to worship what is known,
but to question it.

–Jacob Bronowski, *The Ascent of Man*

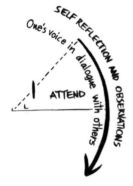

Quadrant 1, Left Mode

Active listening, dialogue and reflection

> Has the student been an active contributor to the group?
>
> Has the student listened?
>
> Has the student assimilated and reflected upon the feelings/thoughts of the other group members?
>
> Has the student expressed his feelings and thoughts?
>
> Has the dialogue helped the student to better understand her position?

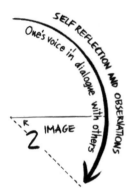

Quadrant 2, Right Mode

Concept congruence

> Are the students' concepts as presented visually and kinesthetically congruent (corresponding) with those of the experts, those the teacher is about to present?
>
> Do the concept presentations show effort and individuality of thought?

Quadrant 2, Left Mode

Knowledge clarity

> Do the students understand the material conceptually? In other words, do they see the big picture, how the parts connect, how the facts relate to the issues?
>
> Do the students see the relationships of the content to real life?
>
> Have they mastered the essentials, the essence material?

Quadrant 3, Left Mode

Skills necessary to proceed

>Has the practice required of the students enabled them to use the material in more personal ways?

>Can they now take what they have learned and place it in the context of real life?

Performance Assessment

Quadrant 3, Right Mode, Quadrant 4, Left and Right Modes

>Has the student used higher order skills in combination with content to:

>solve an interesting problem?

>present an overview of the material?

>raise questions that lead to further study, with originality and flair, acknowledging all sources?

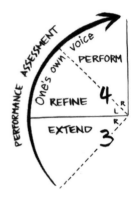

VOICES AROUND THE CYCLE

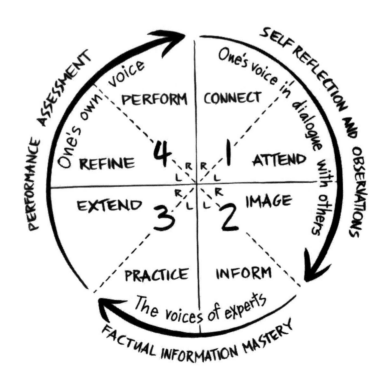

Student Roles as they travel the cycle

As you create your rubrics keep this cycle in mind.

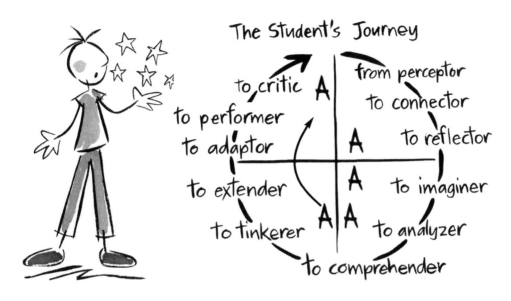

Scoring Considerations for an Assessment Package

☆ Write an assessment package for all five assessment places on the 4MAT wheel: One Left, Two Right, Two Left, Three Left and Four Right. Be sure to include a performance requirement complete with a rubric. Attach a scoring system using the following worksheet.

The formula: (consider doing these tasks with your students)

1. Establish outcomes to be measured.
2. Develop a scoring system
3. Validate your scoring system by collecting exemplary examples of what you want
4. Establish selections regarding what student output will be retained for the portfolio

Share all of the above with your students and parents.

How much is each piece going to count?

Possibilities:

1/3 portfolio, 1/3 standard, 1/3 performance

1/4 portfolio, 1/2 standard, 1/4 performance

Don't forget to ask your students:
"What did you learn that I did not ask you about?"

Please feel free to copy this worksheet.

Assessment Package Scoring System

Use this worksheet to brainstorm Assessment ideas for each of the five Assessment places on the cycle. (Refer to pages 179-180 in this chapter.)

Unit section being assessed: (circle one)

Outcomes

What will your students be expected to know or do after this step?

_____

_____

_____

Selections

What will students produce in this step? Use checklist to indicate if a selection will be included in the student's portfolio.

_____ ☐

_____ ☐

_____ ☐

_____ ☐

Criteria for Judging

Did they know, do and produce what was expected? Will you use letter grades or some other grading system?

☐ Complete/Incomplete

☐ Letter Grade

☐ Numeric Grade

☐ Other _____

Examplars

What are your examplars? Consider work from predecessors and older students. Show what "A" work looks like!

_____

_____

_____

Brainstorm "On the Way" Assessments

_____

_____

Brainstorm "At the Gate" Assessments

_____

_____

A Most Useful Final Assessment for the Students To Complete

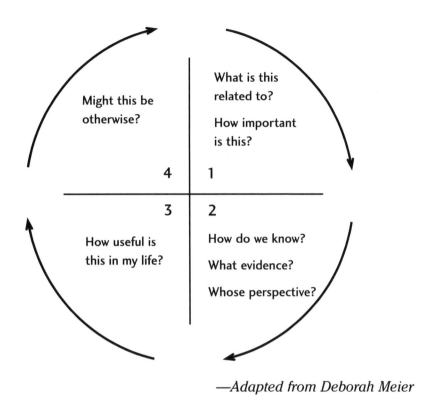

Might this be otherwise?

What is this related to?

How important is this?

4 | 1

3 | 2

How useful is this in my life?

How do we know?

What evidence?

Whose perspective?

—Adapted from Deborah Meier

Try this with your students at the end of a major content section and see what happens—magic happens!

Part Two
Assessing Instruction

The following rubric is presented again to assist teachers in evaluating their instruction according to the 4MAT Framework.

Sample Scaling Criteria

Using the scaling criteria as presented in 4MAT Applications training, the plan's author rates each octant. Ideally, this will occur after the plan has been taught and the teacher has had time to reflect on how the student responded to the unit.

0 = Satisfies the basic requirements

+1 = Indicates a good solid example of this step

+2 = Illustrates a superior or outstanding example

Quadrant One Right Mode

0   The activity connects learners to the concept in a personal way and directly relates to the concept. Non-trivial verbal dialogue is elicited from learners.

+1   Goes to the heart. Allows students to feel their way in a deeper, richer way, an emotional connect.

+2   The experience has a high personal growth potential beyond the immediate experience, possibly multi-modal.

Quadrant One Left Mode

0   Linked to 1R. Feelings about the experience are shared.

+1   Students further explore stated feelings in some way, i.e., listing, patterning, prioritizing or stating their own goals and objectives for learning.

+2   Small group interactive cooperative learning activity where students analyze their collective experiences and produce a group "product".

Quadrant Two Right Mode

0   The concept is transformed into an image using another medium besides words (prose).

+1   The image is moved to a metaview, one that connects the concept by placing it in a larger perspective.

+2   A conceptual "bridge" is created from direct experience to abstract concept. Learners are involved in reflective production, perhaps, visual, kinesthetic, or auditory experience that blends the emotional and the cognitive, yet remains very personal and subjective.

Quadrant Two Left Mode

0   Developmentally appropriate, organized information is transmitted that contains expert treatment of the concept.

+1   Same as above with the addition of appropriate video and/or guest expert.

+2   Interactive instruction (leading learners in transferable future directions) uses multiple methods including visuals and demonstrations, encourages diverse note-taking methods, i.e. mind-mapping sketching as well as traditional means.

Quadrant Three Left Mode

0   Appropriate guided practice, e.g. workbook pages, teacher prepared exercises, etc.

+1 In addition, students use guided practice involving learning centers and using multiple modalities.

+2 Analysis of information now known by students is done individually or in groups. Students have opportunity to look at information in a new way (compare, contrast, problem solve, etc.). In addition, students may create additional multi-modal practice activities and tests to be shared with peers.

Quadrant Three Right Mode

0   Personal "tinkering" is required in some way.

+1 Students have opportunities to design real problems with real-world application and agreed-upon rubrics.

+2 Multiple options for tinkering are available which take into account learning styles, hemisphericity, and modality preferences of learners.

Quadrant Four Left Mode

0   Teacher and students evaluate learning applications for relevance and originality.

+1 Students edit, refine, rework and analyze their own effectiveness.

+2 Facilitates students in "going the extra mile" (input from teacher and peers) to improve their meaningful application of the concept before sharing.

Quadrant Four Right Mode

0   Students report/ demonstrate what they have learned.

+1 Learning is enjoyed and celebrated.

+2 Learners integrate (through some refocusing application, public when possible) and new learning happens. Most students experience strong emotional involvement.

☆ Now, total your scores in each of the quadrants and write the sums below:

Quadrant 3: _____   Quadrant 1: _____

Quadrant 4: _____   Quadrant 2: _____

If your scores are low in any quadrant, consider reviewing the material in the Quadrant chapters for tips on enhancing those elements of your instruction.

*If you don't
change assessment,
nothing changes.*

–Bernice McCarthy

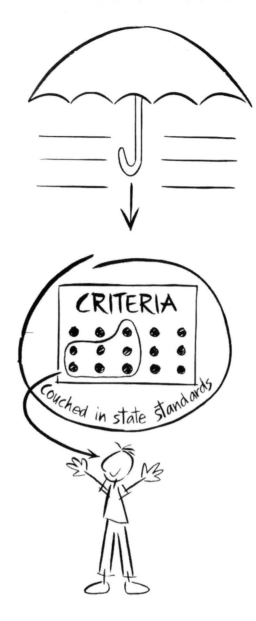

Section Two

Chapters 9-10

4MAT and Curriculum

Chapter Nine

Aligning Standards and Curriculum to Instruction

DEDUCTION

starting from available information

6. Create Essential Questions

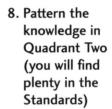

5. Decide on major concepts and build bridges

4. Create instructional timelines

3. Align to resources, (How much of the required material is covered in resources? How much do you have to add?)

2. Characterize and categorize (cluster Standards based on content requirements in meaningful ways)

1. Card index the Standards, paraphrased and considered in terms of learners

INDUCTION

starting from generalization

7. Pattern the connections in Quadrant One (you will have to add your own ideas)

8. Pattern the knowledge in Quadrant Two (you will find plenty in the Standards)

9. Pattern the skills around the cycle (also abundant in the Standards)

10. Pattern the performances in Quadrant Four (you will have to add your own ideas)

11. Enhance around the wheel with music, art, technology, personal development focus, growth process abilities

12. Do assessment, rubrics, portfolio requirements

The following process describes a method for organizing standards under meaningful umbrella concepts then attaching these concepts to instruction. It is a process that can be used...

at the beginning of the school year when strategizing units and curriculum.

by new teachers or experienced teachers to get a sense of how to meaningfully deliver standards in the classroom.

by curriculum committees, to create teacher-friendly and learner-centered curriculum guides.

This process involves determining the essential ideas that overarch the content, then delivering instruction from these central concepts in terms of the principles of 4MAT: learner engagement, rich delivery of content, application to the real world and creative manifestation of material learned.

Deductive vs. Inductive

Consider the graphic at the left. In the first half of this process, teachers and curriculum developers think about the standards and curriculum deductively, like Sherlock Holmes forming generalizations (concepts) from myriad clues (standards, curriculum, texts). The standards are patterned, clustered, characterized and finally conceptualized. These concepts form the starting point for the second half of the process, as these generalizations are applied to instruction.

State and district standards are a great help in this task. Make them work for you rather than letting them overwhelm you. You can cluster standards into manageable form using your own professional judgment and knowledge of your students. Look to the standards as your structuring source. The task is to align the standards with your district's curriculum using the text and other resource materials. Do this with your own particular students in mind, in the particular place and time where you are. What follows is a series of steps to help you in accomplish this task.

Throughout this process, we will reference material from the Indiana fifth grade Social Studies standards. The goal is to create a multi-unit series that incorporates multiple standards and uses concepts as the basis for meaningfully delivering large amounts of content. By building the curriculum with significant concepts, large amounts of content can be meaningfully covered. Look for this icon throughout Chapter Nine.

Indiana Example

Step 1: Card index, categorize and paraphrase the standards

The first step is to card index the standards. Take a pile of 3 x 5 cards, lots of different colored pens and begin. Card indexing involves recording, becoming familiar with and paraphrasing the major skills and content information from each standard. As you write the standards on the cards, priorities will begin to emerge. You must determine what is important to stress and what is not important. Some standards are exciting, foundational and contain vital ideas. Some are small facts or basic skills that are not as essential for students.

Create Piles

As you card index the standards, the categories will become clear. These categories may not be the same as the existing categories. Make piles. If you are a science teacher, you may create a pile of "Cell" standards. If you are a social studies teacher, you may create a pile of "Government" standards. Your brain, and your students' brains need to see large bodies of information in categories. One-by-one is not brain compatible. The process of categorizing standards also helps you become more familiar with them.

And you need to become **very** familiar with your standards. Think about a grocery store, where you've never been. Because you are unfamiliar with the items and layout, you are forced to conduct an item-by-item search for ingredients. However, when you know where things are, you are freed from the distraction of trying to *find* things and are able to think about the bigger picture of your personal needs. Familiarity with the ingredients and layout of your curriculum will allow you to be creative when creating recipes for engaging learners.

Try to be both fascinated and creative when you go through the standards. Let your mind wander a bit, go off on tangents, and feel free to jot down ideas that strike you. In our Indiana example, when we came across the study of Government, we mused, "Why Government at all?" This is a bit of a departure from the technical wording of the standard, but we knew intuitively that this question could form the basis of a rich classroom experience—one that would engage learners.

Chapter Nine: Aligning Standards and Curriculum to Instruction

You may find that standards are delivered somewhat randomly. It is the teacher's job to take:

what she knows about her students,

what she knows about how people learn,

the random standards she is working from and

to deliver the material in a brain-friendly, associative, engaging way, connecting to the learner's meaning and relevance.

IN-SS.5.1   History Students will describe the historical movements that influenced the development of the United States from pre-Columbian times to the end of the eighteenth century with an emphasis on the American Revolution and the founding of the United States.

IN-SS.5.1.1   ... Give examples of how prehistoric Native Americans adapted to and changed the environment, including the location of major settlements, such as Cahokia and Mesa Verde. *Prehistoric: Prior to the use of writing in a given area

IN-SS.5.1.2   ... Identify Native Americans of the West, Southwest, Northwest, Arctic and Sub-Arctic, Great Plains, and Eastern Woodlands regions at the beginning of European exploration and compare their styles of housing, settlement patterns, sources of food and clothing, political and economic organizations, and types and uses of technology. Example: Compare the political organization of the Iroquois Federation to that of Algonquin-speaking peoples.

IN-SS.5.1.3   ... Examine accounts of early European explorations of North America, such as the Vikings? explorations and settlements in Greenland and North America and the interactions between those early Europeans with Native Americans.

IN-SS.5.1.4   ... Describe circumstances in Europe, Africa, and Asia leading to the period of increased contact, exploration, and trade in the 1400s, including advances in the technology of sea travel.

IN-SS.5.1.5   ... Trace the major land and water routes of European explorers of the Caribbean Sea region and North America, and examine their individual stories and reasons for exploration.

IN-SS.5.1.6   ... Identify European nations that sponsored major expeditions. Examples: Spanish expeditions by Christopher Columbus, Hernando Cortes, Hernando de Soto, and Francisco Vasquez de Coronado; expeditions by French explorers Jacques Cartier and Samuel de Champlain; and expeditions for England and Holland by explorers Henry Cabot, Henry Hudson, and John White.

IN-SS.5.1.7   ... Explain the religious, political, and economic reasons for European exploration and colonization, and describe the competition to establish colonies and trade routes.

IN-SS.5.1.8   ... Locate and compare early Spanish, French, and British settlements, such as St. Augustine, Roanoke Island, Quebec, Santa Fe, and Jamestown.

IN-SS.5.1.9   ... Explain events that led people to leave Europe for the Americas, and compare Spanish, French, Dutch, Swedish, Russian, and British colonies in terms of their political, social, and economic purposes and organization.

IN-SS.5.1.10   ... Describe instances of early cooperation and conflict between Native Americans and European settlers, such as agriculture, trade, cultural exchanges, and military alliances, as well as later broken treaties, massacres, and conflicts over control of the land. Example: King Phillip?s War (1675 to 1676) in New England was extremely costly to both sides.

IN-SS.5.1.11   ... Describe the impact of exploration and settlement by Europeans on Native Americans, and analyze conflicts among Native American nations and other factors which led to the Native Americans? defeat by European colonists.

IN-SS.5.1.12   ... Compare and contrast the British, French, and Spanish colonies, in terms of their social and economic organization, religious life, and systems of government, and give examples of how events in Europe impacted life in the Americas.

IN-SS.5.1.13   ... Describe causes, events, and consequences of conflict between the British and French to control territory in North America, which culminated with the British victory in the French and Indian War.

*At this point, your process of prioritization should include any sense you have regarding student performance. If you know for sure that a standard is emphasized on your high-stakes assessment, mark it with a red flag. Some schools are quite proactive about getting assessment results in the hands of teachers for planning purposes. If you know that students struggled with a particular area of the standards on last year's high-stakes assessment, you will want to make a large red flag on your index cards! Later, when designing your units, you can be sure to address these points with your best activities. (Note that some students struggle with material when they do not feel connected to it. It will be your priority to engage them this time around, even if it means "tweaking" your programmed math or reading instruction.) Principals, if your achievement data is not delivered to you in a way that allows teachers to very specifically see areas of strength and weakness, you need to find a way get your data in a more accessible format! Teachers need to examine student achievement data **while** they are working with their students.*

Indiana Example

Our Indiana Example

We begin by examining the list of Social Studies standards that 5th grade teachers are expected to cover. There are fifty-eight Social Studies standards. They include American History as well as Indiana history, geography skills, ideas about market economies and the effects of culture on peoples' lives. We will cluster these fifty-eight standards into a manageable system that could be taught with some depth in the one-year time limit allotted.

Below is our list of paraphrased and categorized standards from the Indiana standards.

History

Why the initial settlers came, who they were

66 days on board the *Mayflower*

Freedom, opportunity, the hardships, landings, indigenous peoples

Early settlements (They could create one perhaps.)

Great leaders: Patrick Henry, Benjamin Franklin

(The standards reflect a need for teachers to

characterize leader(s) forged by the times.)

The American Revolution, causes and results

Timeline from 1650 to 1800

The debate on the Constitution

Geography

Longitude and latitude (There were some map-making standards I knew 10 and 11-year olds would have fun with.)

How location influenced settlements: the land, rivers, mountains, seacoasts, whose land they took

Major cities, rivers, mountains, why cities grew up where they did. (This section had great Quadrant 3, Right Mode possibilities—choices made about a semi-fictitious wilderness where a great city might arise.)

American Indian tribal lands in Indiana. What happened? How fair was it?

Climate considerations, how the land became their survival, transportation issues

Civics/Government

Why do people need government at all?

The three branches, key ideas

The Bill of Rights

Good citizenship

Economics

Market economy, trade and competition

Certain goods: beaver pelts and maple syrup, food (Very interesting sections in the text on these items.)

A personal budget (interesting standards for 5th graders)

Culture and Society

Basic needs of all cultures (Many possible connections here, and revisit the reasons for government perhaps.)

Conflicts and how resolved (comparisons on how we do that today)

Artifact examples, music and folk tales pertinent to Indiana (some wonderful choices in the reading text)

Community formation

In the steps that follow, this familiarity-building and pattern-finding exercise will lead to increasingly sophisticated connections between standards, curriculum, resources and learners.

IN-SS.5.1 History Students will describe the historical movements that influenced the development of the United States from pre-Columbian times to the end of the eighteenth century with an emphasis on the American Revolution and the founding of the United States.

IN-SS.5.1.1 ... Give examples of how prehistoric Native Americans adapted to and changed the environment, including the location of major settlements, such as Cahokia and Mesa Verde. *Prehistoric: Prior to the use of writing in a given area

IN-SS.5.1.2 ... Identify Native Americans of the West, Southwest, Northwest, Arctic and Sub-Arctic, Great Plains, and Eastern Woodlands regions at the beginning of European exploration and compare their styles of housing, settlement patterns, sources of food and clothing, political and economic organizations, and types and uses of technology. Example: Compare the political organization of the Iroquois Federation to that of Algonquin-speaking peoples.

IN-SS.5.1.3 ... Examine accounts of early European explorations of North America, such as the Vikings? explorations and settlements in Greenland and North America and the interactions between those early Europeans with Native Americans.

IN-SS.5.1.4 ... Describe circumstances in Europe, Africa, and Asia leading to the period of increased contact, exploration, and trade in the 1400s, including advances in the technology of sea travel.

IN-SS.5.1.5 ... Trace the major land and water routes of European explorers of the Caribbean Sea region and North America, and examine their individual stories and reasons for exploration.

IN-SS.5.1.6 ... Identify European nations that sponsored major expeditions. Examples: Spanish expeditions by Christopher Columbus, Hernando Cortes, Hernando de Soto, and Francisco Vasquez de Coronado; expeditions by French explorers Jacques Cartier and Samuel de Champlain; and expeditions for England and Holland by explorers Henry Cabot, Henry Hudson, and John White.

IN-SS.5.1.7 ... Explain the religious, political, and economic reasons for European exploration and colonization, and describe the competition to establish colonies and trade routes.

IN-SS.5.1.8 ... Locate and compare early Spanish, French, and British settlements, such as St. Augustine, Roanoke Island, Quebec, Santa Fe, and Jamestown.

IN-SS.5.1.9 ... Explain events that led people to leave Europe for the Americas, and compare Spanish, French, Dutch, Swedish, Russian, and British colonies in terms of their political, social, and economic purposes and organization.

IN-SS.5.1.10 ... Describe instances of early cooperation and conflict between Native Americans and European settlers, such as agriculture, trade, cultural exchanges, and military alliances, as well as later broken treaties, massacres, and conflicts over control of the land. Example: King Phillip?s War (1675 to 1676) in New England was extremely costly to both sides.

Step 2: Characterize and categorize the standards

At some point, you need to look at what the standards represent. Generally speaking, state and district standards can be characterized as **KNOWLEDGE**, **SKILLS**, or **BIG IDEAS**. Depending on the subject area, you will find the standards weighted in one direction or another. For example, Math standards are very skills oriented. Social Studies standards can be very knowledge intensive. (These are easier to test for understanding.)

Using your standards cards (possibly employing a color-coding system) characterize your standards in terms of knowledge, skills, or big ideas. Mark cards with **K**, **S**, or **B.I.** This will help later as you further consider the standards in terms of the elements of 4MAT instruction.

Be careful when characterizing your Knowledge and Skills standards. There are big knowledge/skills and there are small knowledge/skills. Big standards will comprise a major portion of your content delivery and practice (Quadrants Two and Three). Small standards should be included within the context of a larger unit. For example, in a unit on Thornton Wilder, an English teacher asked students to write his resume, satisfying the resume-writing standard without devoting an entire unit to it.

*Hint: Look to the verbs that begin the standard. Words like **describe**, **pattern**, **trace** will more likely lead to big knowledge. Words like **identify**, **list**, **give examples** are more likely to lead to small knowledge or isolated facts.*

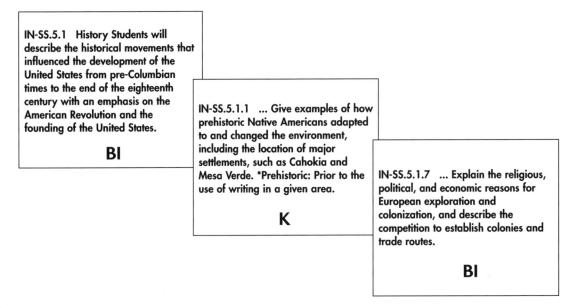

IN-SS.5.1 History Students will describe the historical movements that influenced the development of the United States from pre-Columbian times to the end of the eighteenth century with an emphasis on the American Revolution and the founding of the United States.

BI

IN-SS.5.1.1 ... Give examples of how prehistoric Native Americans adapted to and changed the environment, including the location of major settlements, such as Cahokia and Mesa Verde. *Prehistoric: Prior to the use of writing in a given area.

K

IN-SS.5.1.7 ... Explain the religious, political, and economic reasons for European exploration and colonization, and describe the competition to establish colonies and trade routes.

BI

Back to Indiana

Here is our Indiana list with characterizations regarding which are **Knowledge**, **Skills**, and **Big Ideas**. Note how few skills are marked **(S)**. Social Studies standards tend to have many big ideas and lots of knowledge. In fact, Social Studies makes a great "jumping-off place" to other subject areas. For example, imagine a unit based on an era, supported by Literature, Art, Music, Science and even Math.

Indiana Example

History

Why the initial settlers came **(BI)**,

Who they were

66 days on board the *Mayflower*.

Freedom, opportunity,

The hardships **(all BI)**,

Landings **(K)**

Indigenous peoples **(K)**

Early settlements **(K** - They could create one perhaps**)**

Great leaders: Patrick Henry, Benjamin Franklin **(K or BI** - The standards reflect a need for teachers to characterize a leader(s) forged by the times.**)**

The American Revolution, causes and results **(BI)**

Timeline from 1650 to 1800 **(K)**

The debate on the Constitution. **(K or BI)**

Geography

Longitude and latitude **(S** - There were some map making standards I knew 10 and 11-year olds would have fun with.**)**

How location influenced settlements,

The land,

Rivers,

Mountains,

Seacoasts,

Whose land they took **(K or BI)**

Major cities, rivers, mountains **(K)**,

Why cities grew up where they did. (**BI** - This section had great Quadrant 3, Right Mode possibilities—choices made about a semi-fictitious wilderness where a great city might arise.)

American Indian tribal lands in Indiana. (**K**)

What happened? How fair was it? (**BI**)

Climate considerations, how the land became their survival, transportation issues. (**BI**)

Civics/Government

Why do people need government at all? (**BI**)

The three branches, key ideas (**BI**)

The Bill of Rights (**K or BI**)

Good Citizenship (**BI**)

Economics

Market economy (**K**)

Trade and competition (**K**)

Certain goods: beaver pelts and maple syrup, food (Very interesting sections in the text on these items.)

A personal budget (**S** - interesting standards for 5th graders)

Culture and Society

Basic needs of all cultures (**BI** - Many possible connections here, and revisit the reasons for government perhaps.)

Conflicts and how resolved (**BI** - comparisons on how we do that today)

Artifact examples, music and folk tales pertinent to Indiana (**K** - Some wonderful choices in the reading text.)

Community formation (**BI**)

Step 3: Examine the textbook and other materials available to align the standards to your curriculum

Align the standards with the texts you are using. This comparison of the text and the standards is necessary because teachers need to know how much standard-related material is in their assigned texts.

Some text resources are not aligned to state standards at all. The reverse of this is textbooks that are standards-aligned, but try too hard, delivering too much material too soon and not in the context of the learner.

Consider what materials will support your emerging major units. What material is available in these texts that the standards require, what material is not there, and where will you get the material you need that is not there? Then go outside the school resources and fill in the blanks. Look to the Internet, to resources used in the past, to magazine articles and journals, to current events and media, to new technologies. Consider community members and guest speakers. Consider famous people who may be willing to "visit" your class online.

Jot down resource references on your index cards, both school resources and your own.

Don't limit yourself to subject areas. Use the Reading, Science and Math texts as well as the Social Studies text. As we move further into this process, you will see that defining units conceptually leads to cross-subject thinking. There are particularly strong connections between Math and Science and between Social Studies and Language/English. Using 4MAT, you could hardly design a Social Studies unit without including Literature and the Arts. Even in Math, think about fractions in terms of music, balance in terms of movement, variables in terms of Physics or Computer Programming.

Back to Indiana

In our Indiana example, our examination of the social studies text as well as the reading text, the science text and the math texts revealed that about 60% of what the standards required was contained in those materials. The reading text provided narratives and stories that we found we could use as part of the major units we were beginning to form in our mind based on the Social Studies standards. However, we definitely needed to turn to other sources to cover the content well.

Indiana Example

In this and the previous two steps, you are pattern-finding. Familiarity with your standards, your resources, and with 4MAT will solidify these patterns. You are employing the kind of deductive reasoning that introduced this section.

We subsequently found much of the content we needed on the Internet and in the teacher district resource center. As we reviewed the texts, the resource material and the Internet selections, we enlarged our sense of the clustering possibilities we were considering for our major 4MAT units.

Also, as we read through the Social Studies text we found many things that were not listed in the standards at all. It was clear those parts of the text did not need to be taught. Almost the entire second half of the text contained material that was not included in the standards!

Step 4: Create instructional timelines

A realistic assessment of timelines is critical to covering material effectively. Specifically how much time can you devote to your units? It's common for newer teachers to "bite off more than they can chew." More experienced teachers know that five hours rarely means five hours.

Indiana Example

Our Indiana example and timelines

Our next task was to determine how much time the fifth grade teachers had to cover the required material. The answer was one hour per day. That would be five hours per week. We know how schools work, so we wrote off Friday. Something always happens on Friday. So we figured we had four hours a week.

There are eighteen weeks per semester, but again teachers never get the eighteen weeks. There is Christmas/Chanukah/Kwanza, winter and Easter vacations and so on. With pep rallies, fund drives and required testing there are really only sixteen weeks available for instruction.

Our final decision was to allot two sixteen-week semesters with four hours of instruction time per week. This totaled sixty-four hours per semester or a grand total of one hundred twenty-eight hours in the 5th grade school year to teach the chosen concepts/content/skills for Indiana Social Studies.

Given the limited time and the volume of material to be covered, teachers need to be realistic about what is possible. Experienced teachers do this naturally.

Once we had the clustered standards, and the texts checked out and the time allotted to teach the material, the next step was to make the final decisions on how to conceptualize the content.

Step 5: Conceptualize the content

This is a big step, a very big step. Refer back to the material on concepts in Section One of this workbook to reinforce this critical process in your mind. The key to the entire process of aligning curriculum and instruction using 4MAT is concepts.

In section one, you looked at the Umbrella exercise as a way of discovering the essence that overarches instruction. We now apply this concept of concepts to the task of creating cohesive instruction–instruction that ties it all together–learner connections, knowledge, practice, performance, exciting right mode activities, standards and resources. The glue that holds all of this together is the concept. The concept creates both breadth and depth.

Let us go over the steps so far:

> We listed, paraphrased, clustered and characterized the standards.

> We also examined provided texts and resources and looked to other sources for enhancements.

> We began to characterize standards in terms of knowledge, skills and big ideas.

> If the information was available, we noted which standards would definitely appear on a high-stakes assessment and which standards students struggled with, in terms of assessment results.

As we consider the overarching conceptual ideas, we see that our deductive process has led to generalizations. We will use these generalizations in the second half of the process to attach the concepts and standards to instruction. The umbrella concepts will overarch the standards and our activities and will tie the 4MAT instructional sequence together to form a cohesive whole of learner connections, information, practice and integration.

How we conceptualize content is directly related to how we see the world. We see it our way, from behind our own eyes. We have individual perceptions about the world and we bring these perceptions with us to this task.

Fish is Fish (Lionni, 1970) describes a fish who is keenly interested in learning about what happens on land, but the fish cannot explore land because it can only breathe in water. It befriends a tadpole who grows into a frog and eventually goes out onto the land. The frog returns to the pond a few weeks later and reports on what he has seen. The frog describes all kinds of things like birds, cows, and people. The book shows pictures of the fish's representations of each of these descriptions: each is a fish-like form that is slightly adapted to accommodate the frog's descriptions—people are imagined to be fish who walk on their tailfins, birds are fish with wings, cows are fish with udders. This tale illustrates both the creative opportunities and dangers inherent in the fact that people construct new knowledge based on their current knowledge.

(How People Learn: Brain, Mind, Experience and School, 2000)

The standards give us a list of the content. Think of the standards as the material (ideas and skills) to be taught in Quadrants Two and Three. And see Quadrants One and Four as the place where those ideas and skills are matched to particular students in particular places and times, the place where teacher artistry comes to the fore.

In step one of this process, you considered the standards in terms of their basic categories, for example, Government. Now, we deepen the thinking and consider the standards in light of the concepts that form the *real* essence of what you will teach. These concepts will also from the basis of your learner connections.

In Chapter Two, we presented sample umbrella concepts:

> Content: Christopher Columbus
>
> Umbrella Concept: Exploration

> Content: Photosynthesis
>
> Umbrella Concept: Growth

> Content: The Holocaust
>
> Umbrella Concept: Dehumanization

Now, look at your standards, resources, current events, or outside experts in terms of these enlarged concepts. When considering Dehumanization, how many of these elements can be folded in? When considering Growth, what are the ideas from non-science subject areas that would work? Can you encourage learners to think of Exploration in terms of both Christopher Columbus and nanotechnology?

What do your standards require? What resources are available? What knowledge is "out there in the world"? What is happening *now?* How do all these elements fold together under your umbrella concepts?

This is the key to teacher artistry that is realized within the 4MAT framework. Once you teach yourself to think this way, the transition to instruction: learner connections, knowledge, practice and creative use will unfold naturally and elegantly.

Once you have made decisions regarding Concepts, you are ready to connect the dots. This is an exciting part of the process! In this step, the creation of mindmaps is critical. Your intellectual process can be captured in a way that doesn't stop the creative process. Try creating a central mindmap balloon representing your concept. Then, visit your index cards to find content that could be folded under that concept. (*Inspiration*™ or another computerized mindmapping tool will save a lot of time and may get your creative juices flowing.) For an example, look at our mindmaps of the Indiana Social Studies curriculum. When creating these diagrams, feel free to include more than just the standards. Resources, ideas from external resources and experts, current events, and other subject areas should eventually be "attached" to your major concepts to form the basis for your major units.

When you finish step five, you will have all the dots connected, the big teachable ideas that form the teachable categorizations for the standards and curriculum. Without this big picture, you are facing a one-standard-at-a-time approach, which *cannot* work, either in terms of coverage or long-term, learner understanding.

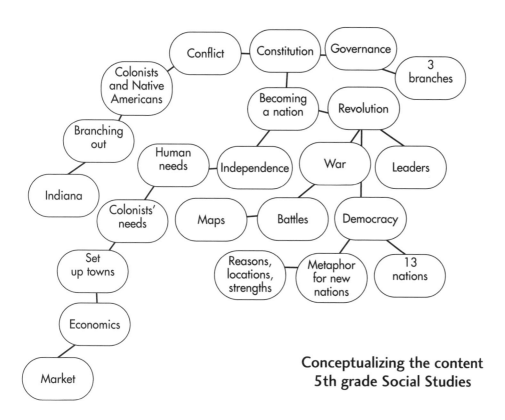

**Conceptualizing the content
5th grade Social Studies**

Indiana Example

Try it in Indiana

We revisited the standards looking at the key issues that were emerging for the four major units we needed to create to bring the most important content to ten-year-old students in Indiana in 2003 using available materials. We chose **Exploration**, **The Land**, **Governance** and **Culture/Conflict**. These choices came from our clustering process using the cards we had indexed, the texts we had examined and the standards we reviewed.

The umbrellas for each of the four units are as follows:

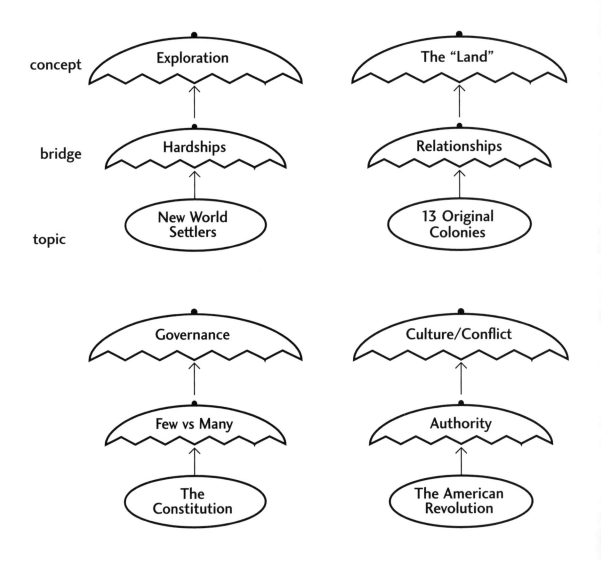

Moving from Deduction to Induction

In the first five steps of this process we thought deductively and moved toward generalizations (the concepts), which emerged from patterns in the content.

In the next seven steps, we think inductively. We move to a "hypothesis" and application (units) based on our generalizations (the concepts). The first half of the process is mostly mental work. The second half of the process is active, the results will be *used*. You will develop "lesson shells" that can be refined for your learners using the tools presented in the first section of this workbook. Curriculum, instruction and learner connections will now begin to come together.

As you develop the specifics from the generalization, it would be helpful to capture the information using technology or a notebook. (Try http://4mat.livetext.com for a tool designed for this purpose!)

6. Create Essential Questions

5. Decide on major concepts and build bridges

4. Create instructional timelines

3. Align to resources, (How much of the required material is covered in resources? How much do you have to add?)

2. Characterize and categorize (cluster Standards based on content requirements in meaningful ways)

1. Card index the Standards, paraphrased and considered in terms of learners

DEDUCTION

starting from available information

INDUCTION

starting from generalization

7. Pattern the connections in Quadrant One (you will have to add your own ideas)

8. Pattern the knowledge in Quadrant Two (you will find plenty in the Standards)

9. Pattern the skills around the cycle (also abundant in the Standards)

10. Pattern the performances in Quadrant Four (you will have to add your own ideas)

11. Enhance around the wheel with music, art, technology, personal development focus, growth process abilities

12. Do assessment, rubrics, portfolio requirements

Voices from the Field

How 4MAT Teachers think about Curriculum and Instruction

I want to share with you some of my recent thinking and research findings on concepts.

When we teach teachers how to identify concepts for instructional units, we have emphasized the content in all of its glorious detail. This definitely leads you to a concept and enriches the value of quadrant 1. In recent research I have been doing on critical thinking, there has been significant emphasis on concepts as patterns that trigger the application of skills. Bransford, Brown, & Cocking (2000) emphasize this in *How People Learn*; these findings have become a major emphasis in the critical thinking research. Because pattern recognition is THE KEY to memory retrieval, it makes sense that it would be crucial for the application/transfer of skills.

As I have been conceptualizing lately, I've not only thought about the details of the content (the 2L piece), but also about how the information will be applied so that my concept represents the pattern that calls for the application. Here's a poor example, but one I'm currently working through:

With a unit on the Solar System in third grade, I could consider the 2L "stuff" and say, "Oh, it's a study in order or cycles, or comparison (sizes, number of moons, etc.)" But none of those really help with how to use the information. So the questions I have to ask as a designer of instruction are, "How will this information be used? What pattern will connect real-life with this content?" This really steers me toward other concepts. In working with this unit I'm wondering how I use what I know about the planets. My answer, though probably too simple, is that I know what is required to sustain life, and I know that those requirements are found only on earth. The characteristics of earth match the needs of living things. So if I am caring for a living thing (including myself), I know that I need to attend to its basic, life-sustaining needs. Which I know (in part) because of having studied the solar system. Now I'm thinking about something like "Necessities" being the concept for the unit. (Like I said, I'm still wrestling with this one.)

Any way, the point is this: for transfer of learning to occur, pattern recognition is key. And I think that the concept is the connection to pattern. So as I design instruction, my thinking about concepts must include the Q3 "stuff" as well as the Q2 "stuff." In fact, the Q3 stuff may be as important (or even more so) than Q2 in the selection of a concept.

Kevin Washburn is a teacher at Briarwood Christian School in Birmingham, Alabama, and a Certified 4MAT Trainer.

Step 6: Create the Essential Question(s)

The Essential Question encompasses what a student should know and be able to do at the end of a unit. This decision determines the essence of the material. The Essential Question is posed to the students at the beginning of the 4MAT unit or lesson. It is the focus throughout the entire learning process.

The Essential Question influences:

> the choice of Quadrant One experiences,
>
> the performance requirements of Quadrant Four,
>
> the Quadrant Two content and
>
> the Quadrant Three skills.

The Essential Question connects all the parts.

4MAT in Action!

Ideas for Determining the Essential Question

Essential Questions are basically extensions of the unit concept. Ask the following of your concept...

> Why does this thing exist?
>
> What or who created this thing?
>
> What connects you to it?
>
> Do you influence it?
>
> Are you influenced by it?
>
> How does this thing work?
>
> What are the pros and cons of this thing?
>
> What would the world be like without this thing?
>
> If this thing seems to occur naturally, what function does it perform?
>
> How does this thing affect the overall balance of the system it contributes to?
>
> Why was this thing invented (either by its creator or by the natural process that demanded it)?

Is the world better or worse off because of this thing?

What are its components? Is it a part of something bigger?

Would something very important be lacking for want of it?

Does it change over the generations? Why?

At the conclusion of Step Six, you should have the Essential Question(s) that will support the concept throughout the unit. Note that in this and the previous step, you are beginning to bridge from curriculum to instruction.

Indiana's Essential Questions

The four essential questions chosen for this year-long, two-semester Social Studies curriculum are:

Indiana Example

Unit One
Concept: Exploration
Essential Question: Why do people explore?
Time Frame: Eight weeks

Unit Two
Concept: The Land
Essential Question: How are we connected to the land? Do we make the land or does the land make us?
Time Frame: Eight weeks

Unit Three
Concept: Governance
Essential Question: Why do people need government? And how does ours work?
Time Frame: Eight weeks

Unit Four
Concept: Culture/Conflict
Essential Question: What are the positives and negatives of conflict?
Time Frame: Eight weeks

Another teacher might have chosen very different questions, reflecting a very different conceptual approach, and one that could be equally good in terms of inspiring the students and equipping them with the knowledge, skills and attitudes planned as the outcomes of these units.

Indiana Example

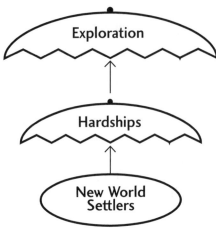

Exploration

Hardships

New World Settlers

Essential Question

Why do people explore?

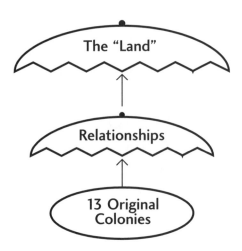

The "Land"

Relationships

13 Original Colonies

Essential Question

How are we connected to the land?
Do we make the land or does the
land make us?

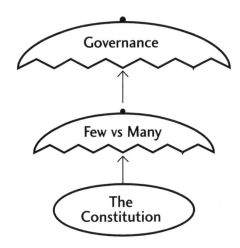

Governance

Few vs Many

The Constitution

Essential Question

Why do people need rules and what is
the process by which rules are created?

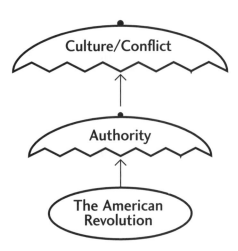

Culture/Conflict

Authority

The American Revolution

Essential Question

What are the positives and
negatives of conflict?

Characterizing Standards in Terms of 4MAT

In the next phase of this process, you will need to place your standards and resources on the 4MAT wheel, further refining your characterization of the standards. From this point on, it will be helpful for you to create large wheels for each of your concepts, with the concept name and essential question in the center. You will then physically place your standards cards onto the quadrants of these large wheels.

Remember, in Texas the standards are actually called "essential knowledge and skills". Imagine yourself as a first grader, knowing that you are about to embark on twelve years of knowledge and skills! Consider it your job to add Quadrant One and Quadrant Four to the "essential knowledge and skills" represented by the standards.

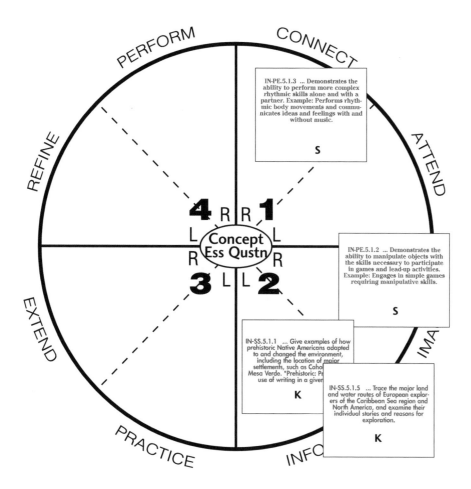

In preparation for this, you must further characterize your standards.

In step two of this process, you characterized your standards in terms of **Knowledge**, **Skills** and **Big Ideas**. Now we will add two more characteristics: learner **Connections** and **Performances**. Which standards do you think will connect well to learners? What are their interests? What will they consider "fun"? Return to your standards index cards and use a special highlighter color for these items, perhaps yellow for Connections and light blue for Performances. When you're done you will have only a few Connection or Performance highlights. Standards do not emphasize personal connections and student personal adaptations.

Subjects lend themselves to certain types of standards. You will find that Social Studies emphasizes knowledge. In Math you will find many skills. In Science, you will find a mixture of skills and knowledge. In Language Arts you will find a skills emphasis in the lower grades and a knowledge emphasis as you move up into high school. Language and Literature are the two subjects where you will be likely to find standards OTHER than skills and knowledge.

IN-SS.5.1 History Students will describe the historical movements that influenced the development of the United States from pre-Columbian times to the end of the eighteenth century with an emphasis on the American Revolution and the founding of the United States.

BI

IN-SS.5.1.1 ... Give examples of how prehistoric Native Americans adapted to and changed the environment, including the location of major settlements, such as Cahokia and Mesa Verde. *Prehistoric: Prior to the use of writing in a given area

K

IN-SS.5.1.7 ... Explain the religious, political, and economic reasons for European exploration and colonization, and describe the competition to establish colonies and trade routes.

BI

 **Worksheet: Practice with Real Standards**

Social Studies

☐ **IN-SS.5.1.1**

Give examples of how prehistoric Native Americans adapted to and changed the environment, including the location of major settlements, such as Cahokia and Mesa Verde. *Prehistoric: Prior to the use of writing in a given area.

☐ **IN-SS.5.1.2**

Identify Native Americans of the West, Southwest, Northwest, Arctic and Sub-Arctic, Great Plains, and Eastern Woodlands regions at the beginning of European exploration and compare their styles of housing, settlement patterns, sources of food and clothing, political and economic organizations, and types and uses of technology. Example: Compare the political organization of the Iroquois Federation to that of Algonquin-speaking peoples.

☐ **IN-SS.5.1.3**

Examine accounts of early European explorations of North America, such as the Vikings explorations and settlements in Greenland and North America and the interactions between those early Europeans with Native Americans.

☐ **IN-SS.5.1.4**

Describe circumstances in Europe, Africa, and Asia leading to the period of increased contact, exploration, and trade in the 1400s, including advances in the technology of sea travel.

☐ **IN-SS.5.1.5**

Trace the major land and water routes of European explorers of the Caribbean Sea region and North America, and examine their individual stories and reasons for exploration.

*Directions:
Try characterizing the following random list of standards in terms of which are **Knowledge**, which are **Skills**, which are **Big Ideas**, which might **Connect** to learners and which might make good **Performance** elements. Mark a **K, S, BI** in the space provided. Then, using your colored markers, highlight **Connections** and **Performances**.*

☐ **IN-SS.5.1.6**

Identify European nations that sponsored major expeditions.
Examples: Spanish expeditions by Christopher Columbus, Hernando
Cortes, Hernando de Soto, and Francisco Vasquez de Coronado;
expeditions by French explorers Jacques Cartier and Samuel de
Champlain; and expeditions for England and Holland by explorers
Henry Cabot, Henry Hudson, and John White.

Language Arts

☐ **IN-LA.WR.5.1.1**

Read aloud grade-appropriate narrative text (stories) and expository
text (information) fluently and accurately and with appropriate
timing, changes in voice, and expression.

☐ **IN-LA.WR.5.1.2**

Use word origins to determine the meaning of unknown words.

☐ **IN-LA.WR.5.1.3**

Example: After listening to a story of the myth of Hercules when it is
read aloud, use the knowledge of the story to understand the
phrase Herculean task.

☐ **IN-LA.WR.5.1.4**

Understand and explain frequently used synonyms (words with the
same meaning), antonyms (words with opposite meaning), and
homographs (words that are spelled the same but have different
meanings).

☐ **IN-LA.WR.5.1.5**

Know less common roots (graph = writing, logos = the study of) and
word parts (auto = self, bio = life) from Greek and Latin and use this
knowledge to analyze the meaning of complex words (autograph,
autobiography, biography, biology).

Math

☐ **IN-MTH.5.1.1**

Convert between numbers in words and numbers in figures, for numbers up to millions and decimals to thousandths; Example: Write the number 198.536 in words.

☐ **IN-MTH.5.1.2**

Round whole numbers and decimals to any place value; Example: Is 7,683,559 closer to 7,600,000 or 7,700,000? Explain your answer.

☐ **IN-MTH.5.1.3**

Arrange in numerical order and compare whole numbers or decimals to two decimal places by using the symbols for less than (<), equals (=), and greater than (>); Example: Write from smallest to largest: 0.5, 0.26, 0.08.

☐ **IN-MTH.5.1.4**

Interpret percents as a part of a hundred. Find decimal and percent equivalents for common fractions and explain why they represent the same value; Example: Shade a 100-square grid to show 30%. What fraction is this?

☐ **IN-MTH.5.1.5**

Explain different interpretations of fractions: as parts of a whole, parts of a set, and division of whole numbers by whole numbers; Example: What fraction of a pizza will each person get when 3 pizzas are divided equally among 5 people?

Science

(may turn out differently because of inconsistencies in methods, materials, and observations)

☐ **IN-S.5.1.2**

Begin to evaluate the validity of claims based on the amount and quality of the evidence cited.

IN-S.5.1.3

Explain that doing science involves many different kinds of work and engages men, women, and children of all ages and backgrounds.

IN-S.5.1.4

Give examples of technology, such as telescopes, microscopes, and cameras, that enable scientists and others to observe things that are too small or too far away to be seen without them and to study the motion of objects that are moving very rapidly or are hardly moving.

IN-S.5.1.5

Explain that technology extends the ability of people to make positive and/or negative changes in the world.

Music

Lastly, we look at a Music standard. Music is interesting because it epitomizes skills gained from knowledge. Note in the standard below, performance is the primary focus, with the knowledge almost "assumed". The performance represents the culmination of knowledge and skills, filtered through the learner (our definition of learning).

IN-M.S.5.1

Students sing alone or in groups, on pitch and in rhythm, using good tone, diction, breath control and posture while maintaining a steady tempo. They sing from memory a variety of song repertoire, including ostinatos, partner songs, rounds, and music of many cultures and styles. They sing accurately with appropriate dynamics, breath control, phrasing, and interpretation. Students in Grade 5 sing in groups, blending vocal sounds, matching dynamics, and following the conductor.

☆ Should all knowledge lead to performance? Discuss with a peer.

4MAT in Action! Arranging Standards Around the Cycle

☆ Next you will try this with your own standards and instruction. What you are creating is a shell of a 4MAT lesson, a preparation. Generally speaking, the connections could fit in the Quadrant One of your unit, the knowledge into Quadrant Two, the skills into Quadrant Three, and the performances into Quadrant Four, but please note that these are not hard and fast rules. As you refine the unit, use your discretion to shuffle these around, e.g., placing a skill standard into the performance phase of your lesson. On the following pages, we offer additional details on how to assign these elements around the 4MAT quadrants.

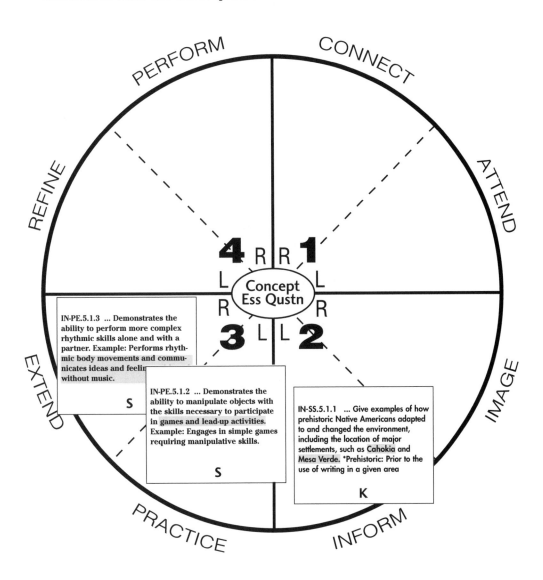

IN-PE.5.1.3 ... Demonstrates the ability to perform more complex rhythmic skills alone and with a partner. Example: Performs rhythmic body movements and communicates ideas and feeling without music.

IN-PE.5.1.2 ... Demonstrates the ability to manipulate objects with the skills necessary to participate in games and lead-up activities. Example: Engages in simple games requiring manipulative skills.

IN-SS.5.1.1 ... Give examples of how prehistoric Native Americans adapted to and changed the environment, including the location of major settlements, such as Cahokia and Mesa Verde. *Prehistoric: Prior to the use of writing in a given area

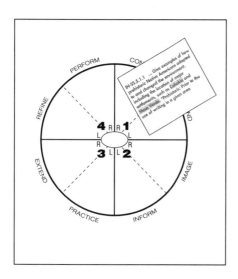

Step 7: Pattern the Connections in Quadrant One
Now we use our standards-to-quadrant alignment skills with your own curriculum. After determining the **Concept**, the **Essential Question**, and the **Content** to be covered, it is time to consider the **Context**—the unique environment where learners work and live.

Revisit the highlighted **Connection** items to check for possible opening activities that might help introduce your concepts. Using your poster-sized, concept-based 4MAT wheels, place the learner **Connection** cards in Quadrant One. If the Connection was a portion of a card, then break it out, create a new card which you will use in Quadrant One. (It is helpful to refer to your mindmap for ideas regarding relationships of concepts to the more discrete pieces.) Since learner connection is not an emphasis of the standards, now is a great time to brainstorm ideas for learner connections not found in the standards and to create new cards to supplement the Quadrant One of your large wheels.

The standards and textbooks will sometimes try to present activities for learner engagement, but in the absence of an instructional framework, the result is often superficial.

What activities will help connect the concept and content to learners? Looking at the concept (the heart of the material to be learned) and considering the Essential Question (which encompasses the end goal of the unit) what teaching strategies will help achieve the instructional goals?

It's important to remember that Quadrant One rarely contains actual **CONTENT**. In Quadrant One, you create an experiential activity that holds meaning for learners, based on their prior experience or knowledge. You are getting them to know what they know, but at a feeling level.

In Quadrant One, we strive to clarify the reason behind the learning. We mutually address the question Why? Quadrant One involves creating an experience that relates **the concept to learners**. The goal is to imbue the experience with meaning so learners are able to see connections to their own experience. These common experiences become a basis for sharing and discussion. It's important to encourage learners to identify and express personal feeling, values and beliefs relative to the concept through simulations, personal examples retold and inventories in which idiosyncratic approaches can be shared.

In Quadrant One...

CONNECT learners directly to the concept in a personal way.

Capture learners' attention by initiating a group problem-solving activity before delivery of instruction.

Begin with a situation that is familiar to learners building on what they already know.

Construct a learning experience that allows diverse and personal responses.

Facilitate the work of cooperative teams of learners.

Elicit non-trivial dialogue.

Guide learners to reflection and analysis of the experience.

Encourage learners to share and examine perceptions and beliefs.

Summarize and review similarities and differences.

Establish a positive attitude toward the diversity of different experiences.

Clarify the reason for the learning.

Refer to Section One of this workbook for a more detailed look at enhancing instruction in Quadrant One.

Indiana Students on a Distant Planet

One of the concepts from our Indiana example is Governance. The Essential Question for the concepts is, "Why do people need rules and what is the process by which rules are created?" In our opening activity that introduces this concept, students are told that they will be colonizing a distant planet and will be the only sentient beings on the planet. They must establish three rules that will allow the new population to get along and thrive. Later in the unit, they'll compare their rules to the *Bill of Rights* (which is of course in the standards).

This example clearly illustrates how the standards are a starting point. The teacher artistry, the delivery of the standards in a way that engages learners is what really matters in terms of performance. A common weakness of 4MAT units created by less experienced teachers is a Quadrant One experience that is lacking in poignancy. To discuss the need for rules is not as compelling as a full experience. Think of ways to engage learners *fully*. You'll know by the energy in the room if you succeeded.

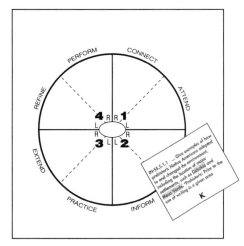

Step 8: Pattern the Knowledge in Quadrant Two

When looking at the standards and text, you probably had no difficulty finding standards that are considered **Knowledge** (and plenty of skills, which we address in the next section). In this next step, starting from concepts, consider your standards in terms of which knowledge standards will fit under which concepts. Using your concept-based 4MAT wheel posters, return to your standards cards and place the knowledge cards in Quadrant Two.

Some of your knowledge standards will fit nicely as small components of a much larger unit. Some may become the central theme of major units. For example, when considering "**Exploration**" in Social Studies, there are many standards under this large umbrella. Be careful to stay in the context of the learner. No single step of a 4MAT unit should exist independently. If you keep your major units interrelated, learners *will* perform. Quadrant One is based on concepts relating to learner connections. Quadrant Two should revisit Quadrant One (information growing out of need).

Quadrant Three should grow from Quadrant Two (practice that involves testing and interpreting knowledge). Quadrant Four should revisit all the quadrants (creative expression that represents the culmination of knowledge and skills).

So the concept not only unites the standards, resources and related content, it holds the instruction together.

Quadrant Two takes learners straight to the heart of conceptual information. It is here where they learn the knowledge base, the content. A good quadrant 2 activity will...

> Provide "acknowledged body of knowledge".
>
> Emphasize significant aspects of the concept in an organized manner.
>
> Present information sequentially so learners see the continuity.
>
> Draw attention to important, discrete details; attempting not to swamp learners with myriad facts.
>
> Use a variety of delivery systems: teacher-directed lecture, interactive lecture (with dialogue), text, guest speakers, films, and demonstrations.

Place into Quadrant Two the standards and resources alignments that emphasize **Knowledge**. The question here becomes, "What do you want learners to know?" The question in the next section is, "What should learners be able to do?"

For a more detailed presentation of enhancing your unit in Quadrant Two, see Chapter Four of this workbook.

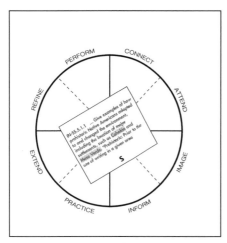

Step 9: Pattern the Skills Around the Cycle

While knowledge and facts seem to generally land in Quadrant Two, skills are not as simple to characterize. The emphasis of Quadrant Three, in regard to instruction is enabling learners to *do* something they couldn't do before. And when analyzing the skills-oriented standards, you will see many skills would work well in Quadrant Three. But it would be an oversimplification of 4MAT to suggest that *all* skills should be considered as Quadrant Three elements.

Skills standards have a magical quality. They can be easily transformed into classroom activities that support all of the 4MAT framework. For example, all standards have speaking and listening skills that align perfectly with the Quadrant One emphasis on peer-to-peer discussion. Many of the skills would fit wonderfully into the performances of Quadrant Four. So, in this step, we will NOT ask you to place your skills standards in the quadrant three of your poster-sized wheel.

Indiana Example

Let's look back to Indiana for an example of this.

Indiana 5th grade skills include all the content areas with special emphasis on Language Arts, Science and Math. As we began to fill in the 4MAT Wheels, we used the lists of these skills to create the activities that would afford the best student practice.

Some examples

In Language Arts

> Recognize main ideas and assess evidence to support them
>
> Draw inferences from texts
>
> Use features of texts, graphics, diagrams, charts, maps
>
> Analyze texts
>
> Distinguish facts vs. opinions
>
> Use good note-taking skills
>
> Write information pieces
>
> Review and edit

Read historical documents, including diaries, journals

Grammar, punctuation and capitalization standards

Oral communication skills

In Science

Environmental standards relating to creating physical settings and interdependence

In Geography

Maps, latitude, longitude

How to use rivers as highways and navigation issues

In Economics

How early settlers used money and its equivalent

How to get food, how to find water

The pricing of furs, the maple syrup business

In Math

Computation skills and measurement techniques as part of problem-solving techniques

The lists of skills sparked our imagination. As we built in the four points on the cycle that 4MAT requires: **reflection, knowledge critiquing, acting on the learning** and **integrating it**, the lists of skills gave us lots of ideas as to what kinds of activities to design.

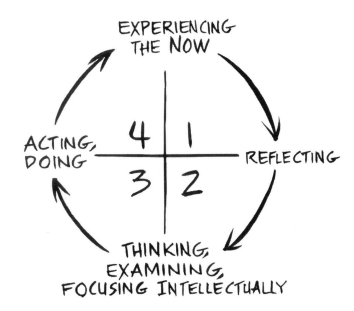

Important Note on Quadrant Three
While you will find many, many standards that are characterized as skills, particularly in math, science and writing, they may not be enough. You MUST establish the real-world usefulness of what you teach. Your priority as a teacher may be very different than the priorities of the authors of the standards. These extensions may be absent from your standards and curriculum documents. Remember, the movement from Quadrant Three to Quadrant Four represents a movement away from standards and accountability back to learner performance and teacher facilitation.

For example, having the students read actual historical diaries and take on the persona of the writers, then journaling their reflections on what it might have been like to be there in that time. (Reflection at 3 o'clock)

Understanding the hardships early settlers had to overcome. (Knowledge critiquing at 6 o'clock)

Building their own Jamestown settlement— how to get water, how to make soap, how to clear a forest, how to build a latrine—material all available on the Internet and explained in 1640 technology. (Acting on the learning at 9 o'clock)

Final papers from both groups and individuals, complete with illustrations on how to understand the present by experiencing, understanding and acting on the knowledge of the past. (Integrating at 12 o'clock)

For a more detailed presentation of enhancing your unit in Quadrant Three, see Chapter Five of this workbook.

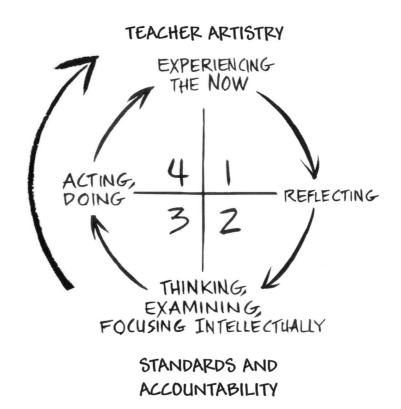

Step 10: Pattern the Performance in Quadrant Four

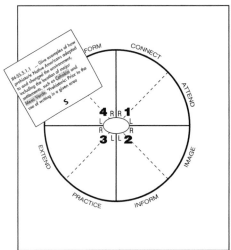

In Quadrant Four of the 4MAT lesson planning process, learners must re-present learning. They share personal adaptations of the material with others and speak in their own voice. Without this step, there is no real learning. Only by representing what they've come to know can learners truly come to understand.

Revisit the highlighted **Performance** items to check for possible culminating activities. If the Performance was a portion of a card, then break it out and create a new card which you will use in Quadrant Four. Using your poster-sized concept-based 4MAT wheels, place the learner Performance cards in Quadrant Four. It will be helpful to refer to your mindmap for ideas regarding relationships of concepts to the more discrete pieces. Since learner Performance is not an emphasis of the standards (beyond the high-stakes assessment), now is a great time to brainstorm ideas for learner Performances and to create new cards to supplement the Quadrant Four of your large wheels.

For a more detailed presentation of enhancing your unit in Quadrant Four, see Chapter Six of this workbook.

For guidance when brainstorming ideas for Quadrant Four, return to your Concept. For example, if Exploration is your concept, how can learners demonstrate an integration of their new Exploration knowledge and skills with a performance?

A good quadrant 4 activity will...

Give guidance and feedback; encouraging, assisting and suggesting refinements.

Help learners analyze their use of the learning for meaning, relevance and originality.

Maintain high expectations for completion of chosen options.

Help turn mistakes into learning opportunities.

Summarize by reviewing the whole learning sequence.

Establish a classroom atmosphere that celebrates all new learning, even failures.

Give learners the support they need to teach and share with others.

Make learner creations available to the larger community: their own books, the information discovered through interviews, their visuals, their demonstrations, the results of their experiments, their family histories illustrated, the scientific findings of local environmental surveys and so on.

Leave learners intrigued by further possible applications of the concept, extending "What Ifs?" into the future, into new cycles.

Step 11: Enhance around the wheel with music, art, technology, personal development focus and growth process abilities

Now, brainstorm ideas for enhancing your unit with rich, engaging activities. This is where the 4MAT wheels really take on a rich and variegated texture.

Add Music and Art

The role of the music and art teacher is gradually undergoing a transformation. When music and art are integrated into the regular classroom, you have opportunities for learners to see material in ways that are visceral and long-lasting. If a primary objective is performance on state and national assessments, the role of music and art in recall is well documented. Consider "setting the stage" using all kinds of art. Imagine the teacher who renders a dramatic reading of *The Gettysburg Address* in period clothing, with Copland accompanying. The arts enable people to step into a scene. Clearly, "being there" will lead to greater engagement, resonance, interest levels and retention. So buy your music and art teachers a cup of coffee and talk to them about your lessons.

Indiana Example

Music, Art and our Social Studies Example

What were:

       the stories they told,

       the songs they sang,

       the dances they danced,

       the art they created,

       the traditional arts and crafts of the early colonists,

       the folk tales and narratives?

Art tells a great story. And there it was on the Internet. We found twenty-four works of art by Sidney King depicting the first winter in Jamestown. One of the assignments we gave the students was for them to enter certain pictures and relate in journal form what it was like to spend an hour there. Think of the richness of the art of a people, their music, their stories.

Add Personal Development Focus

The standards are not completely devoid of Quadrant One. Some standards sets include personal development items that can enrich units in many ways (and places).

Students need to examine how people deal with the obstacles and difficulties they encounter. The gift of metacognition, so crucial to all learning, needs to be a goal in our instructional designs, and the content listed in the personal development standards lends itself beautifully to this goal.

Personal Development Focus in Indiana

In our Indiana example, we took the most often cited characteristics in the personal development standards from key states and built them into the activities for the units. For example, character analysis, instances of great courage, the values held by the people exemplified in their actions.

Indiana Example

The personal development characteristics we used from the composite of state curricula were:

- self-awareness
- relationships
- curiosity
- persistence
- competence
- creativity
- integrity and its concomitant responsibility
- citizenship and its concomitant service.

Add Growth Process Abilities

In addition to the personal development attributes, there are important process abilities to consider in any design for a unit or lesson. These are the processes humans face as they grow and develop. Learners need to examine these processes in terms of living well as they go through their learning experiences. Again, we chose these processes from a composite of standards from key states.

We integrated these processes into discussions of content, current event information and personal story-telling.

Growth processes include:

>   making healthy choices
>
>   dealing with conflict
>
>   being flexible
>
>   making decisions
>
>   practicing habits of reflection.

Add Technology

Technology is an essential addition to any unit. Using 4MAT as a framework for appropriately employing technology will enhance its overall contribution to the learning. For example...

Resources that tell (video, the Internet, informational CD's/DVD's) work very well to add some spice to Quadrant Two. Also in Quadrant Two, as teachers seek out additional expert knowledge, the Internet modernizes the concept of guest lecturer. In many cases, you can find the ultimate authority on any given subject, many of whom are happy to enter your classroom using technology.

Step 12: Do assessment, rubrics, portfolio requirements

Now make your choices as to where to assess on the cycle. Examine this definition of assessment and the assessment wheel in terms of the different kinds of assessments that make up a complete learning process.

Assessment is a conversation I have with myself. It is the intrinsic motivation that guides my growth.

It is a conversation that takes place first, with me as I receive the world, second, with others as we share our worlds, third, between my teachers and me as I learn from the experts and finally, it is the conversation between myself and my work in the world.

This final conversation is the one that ultimately governs my life.

For this conversation to be successful, I must listen to my inner voice, the one that knows.

If there is a destiny beckoning for each of us, who can live it in out stead?

–Bernice McCarthy, 2000

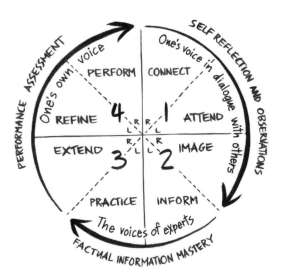

VOICES AROUND THE CYCLE

For a detailed discussion of 4MAT assessment methods, refer to Chapter Eight of this workbook.

The 4MAT checklist

Complete the unit with the following check on your design.

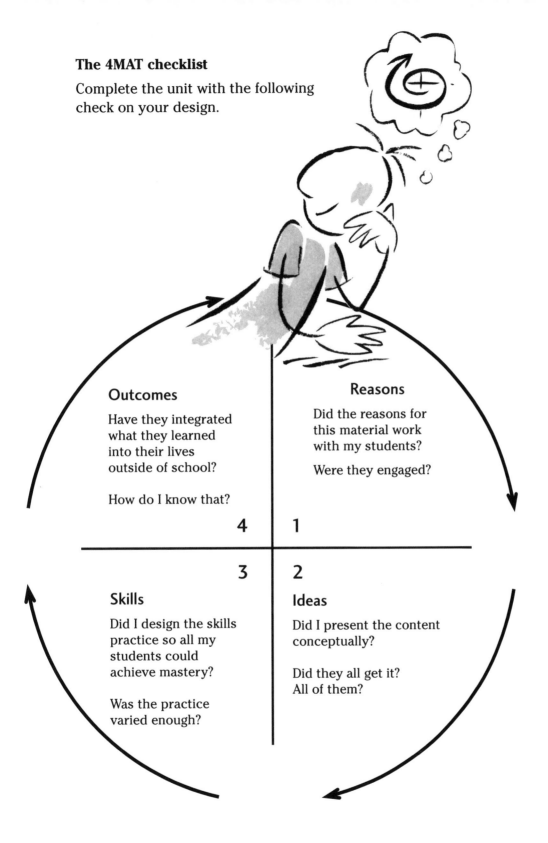

Outcomes

Have they integrated what they learned into their lives outside of school?

How do I know that?

4

Reasons

Did the reasons for this material work with my students?

Were they engaged?

1

3

Skills

Did I design the skills practice so all my students could achieve mastery?

Was the practice varied enough?

2

Ideas

Did I present the content conceptually?

Did they all get it? All of them?

Chapter Ten

Another Look at the Theory and the Research

The Fundamentals of 4MAT Revisited

Humans learn and develop through continuous, personal adaptations as they construct meaning in their lives.

The Underlying Theory Revisited

This section lists some of the work of the major researchers who form the theoretical structure of 4MAT. It is helpful for teams of teachers to examine these findings to deepen their understanding of 4MAT's underlying learning theory.

A one-to-one correspondence between these researchers would oversimplify. Jung deals with the wholeness of personality, Kolb with the perceiving and processing dimensions of learning, Dewey with the interaction of the person with the world of doing, while 4MAT focuses on those behaviors related to the learning process itself.

Note the resolution of opposites is consistent throughout the models. This notion of "oppositeness" is key to understanding the cycle and helping students stretch to all places on the cycle and more fully realize their potential.

Carl Jung

Jung's theory of personality types assumes the presence of measurable and consistent individual preferences for making sense of the world. Jung postulated that much apparent random variation in human behavior is actually orderly and consistent and due to basic differences in the ways people prefer to perceive and judge.

Jung's definitions of the four terms he uses are as follows:

feeling—the process of appreciation in terms of personal value

thinking—a process of logical decision-making

sensing—a process by which the senses tell you something is concrete and exists

intuiting—a process of gauging possibilities by way of insight

Jung claims these functions are opposing ways of making sense of the world.

Perception

Intuitive Types

Intuition directed

Emphasis on possibilities and imagination

Feeling Types

Feeling directed

Emphasis on values and personal friendships

Extroversion ——————————————————————— Introversion

Sensing Types

Body directed

Emphasis on details and concrete events

Thinking Types

Intellect directed

Emphasis on order, analysis or logic

Judgement

☆ Why would these personality types be opposites?

☆ How is judgment the opposite of perception?

☆ Examine the opposite types—how is the "Feeling Type" the opposite of the "Sensing Type" ?

☆ How is the "Thinking Type" the opposite of the "Intuitive Type"?

☆ What do you make of the idea that by going to your shadow side (your least favorite place on the cycle) you afford yourself the opportunity to learn a great deal, and to move into enlarged energy?

ACTING, DOING ———————— REFLECTING

Jung used the terms **extroversion** and **introversion** to describe two basic attitudes toward the environment. Extroverts are individuals who focus their attention on objects and people in the environment. Introverts focus on the energy within themselves. He stated that these two differences were so profound that no one who favored one could ever stretch to the gracefulness of the other. He called them *"antagonistic standpoints which must be viewed as two totally different orientations."*

Yet he was adamant to point out that personal development was the result of the interaction of the two attitudes, the internal subjective of a person (the 3 o'clock place) with the external circumstances of the environment (the 9 o'clock place).

Reflections on Jung

☆ What does this mean for those who prefer the 3 o'clock place or the 9 o'clock place?

Jung's contributions subsequently became formalized by Isabel Myers resulting in the Myers-Briggs Type Indicator® used today throughout the world to examine personality types. Our Learning Type Measure® was normed with the Myers-Briggs as well as the Kolb Learning Styles Indicator®.

☆ What does it mean for those of us who seldom venture over to the "other" side?

☆ Why do you think researchers claim that achieving a balance of the two is one of the keys to mental health?

David Kolb

Kolb classified individuals into one of four learning styles based on a measure of their preferences for perceiving and processing information and experience.

He described a process through which these four modes are engaged at various levels of complexity. He held that as we adapt to the environment, we start with our perceptions and then move to further observations and reflections. We construct a theory based on these perceptions and proceed to test our theories. We examine the results and move to integrate what we have learned or to discard it depending on the outcome.

In both cases, learning has happened.

This process when continued on through growth and development, moves individuals to higher and higher levels of complexity. According to Kolb, *"Individuals expand their learning and adaptive processes through exercising them."*

Note the opposites working here as well.

Concrete Experience

Accomodators

Rely on concrete experiences and process actively

Reduce the complexity of serious analysis in favor of "seeing what happens"

Divergers

Rely on concrete experience and process reflectively

Turn aside the need for quick decisions

Active Experimentation

Reflective Observation

Convergers

Rely on workability of theories which they process actively

Tend to ignore others in tackling problems

Assimilators

Rely on theory and abstract conceptualization which they process reflectively

Reduce the need for creative complexity through strict adherence to data

Abstract Conceptualization

Kolb's work brought learning styles to the forefront in management training circles. His *Learning Styles Indicator*® on which our *Learning Type Measure*® was normed is used by many organizations in the management field.

His contribution to the legitimacy of diversity has had positive impact in the education field bringing validity to the claims regarding the differences in how people learn.

Some of Kolb's Finding Regarding Occupations

Elementary Education	Social Work
Marketing	Nursing
Business	Psychiatry
Accounting	Secondary Education
Engineering	Finance
Medicine	Academics

Reflections on Kolb

☆ Hunch why these occupations tend to favor these places on the cycle.

☆ Why do you think education has long ignored, and in many cases continues to ignore, the importance of concrete experience in the educational experience?

John Dewey

"Human experience is the gateway to understanding."

For John Dewey, schools were testing grounds for thought. Creating and testing ideas through experience was the role of the school—testing the practical consequences of ideas. Dewey's main tenet was that all learning requires the interaction of the person with the world. It is learning by doing, not learning by rote.

History credits Dewey with the introduction of a pedagogy, a teaching method, which united mind and body, through experiencing, observing, thinking and doing. He called it **The Art of Education** and stated it was a supreme art form.

Dewey held cognitive potential is not hidden in the mind awaiting perfection; rather it evolves and diversifies through use.

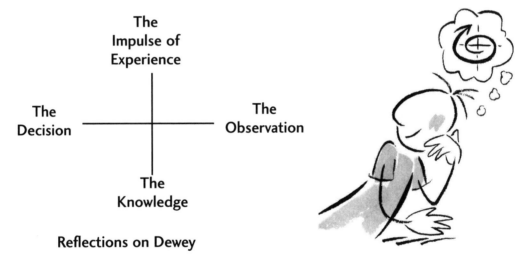

The
Impulse of
Experience

The
Decision

The
Observation

The
Knowledge

Reflections on Dewey

☆ If Dewey was right about how we must use what we learn to truly learn it, why have educators tended to reduce "hands-on" learning to a less exalted place in the hierarchy of learning strategies?

☆ Is it intellectual snobbishness to not require "usefulness?" Is it a fear of how to assess this kind of learning? Is it a lack of professional teacher training regarding how to design performance assessment?

Some Recent Research for Examination

On the following pages I have listed some research we find interesting and thought provoking. Discuss these with your small groups.

Engineering Students Learning Styles

L.E. Bernold, 1999
North Carolina State

Engineering Students = 55

Type Fours	**Type Ones**
4 or 7%	3 or 6%
Type Threes	**Type Twos**
30 or 54%	18 or 33%

The Type One students received the most Fs.

The Type Two students received the most As and Bs. (66%)

☆ What is your reaction to this data?

☆ Are the students the problem here?

High At-Risk Students in a Juvenile Facility

One Teacher's Results

Kearney and Thacker, 1994

July to August used 4MAT lessons

Number of students = 65 and their grades

A's	3
B's	30
C's	28
D's	5
F's	2

September to October returned to traditional instruction

Number of students = 68 and their grades

A's	0
B's	7
C's	18
D's	27
F's	13

January to February returned to 4MAT lessons

Number of students = 58 and their grades

A's	9
B's	42
C's	10
D's	4
F's	3

The new science of complexity essentially claims that the link between cause and effect is difficult to trace, that change (planned and otherwise) unfolds in non-linear ways, that paradoxes and contradictions abound and that creative solutions arise out of interactions under conditions of uncertainty, diversity and instability.

—Michael Fullan

☆ Given Fullan's statement, what would you do with possible cause and effect here if you were the supervisor of the above institution?

Some Data on Public Health Nurses

Wedeking, 2000

N = 106 Public Health Nurses

From Iowa, Minnesota, North Dakota, South Dakota and Wisconsin

72% of them held Baccalaureate degrees in nursing

Type Fours	Type Ones
12%	44%
Type Threes	**Type Twos**
19%	17%

(8% reported they were two or more styles.)

☆ What do you hunch from this data?

Some Data on Teacher Off-Task Behavior

Hancock, 2000

Baylor University

N = 3 classroom teachers

5th, 6th and 7th grade classrooms

Observed over a 20 day period by three trained observers to obtain data describing the actual number of times each teacher was off-task in a 25-minute period.

Off-task behavior was defined as "any redirection of teacher attention by a students that pulls the teacher's focus from the topic currently being taught."

The program under review was 4MAT.

A substantial reduction in the number of off-task behaviors was found when teachers were using The 4MAT System.

☆ What conclusions can you make or not make concerning this data?

☆ Would any teacher focus on a particular pedagogy possibly have the same results?

Data on Teacher Questioning Habits

Kvalo, 1998

A teacher being trained in 4MAT began paying attention to how she used the four quadrant questions, Why? What? How? and If? Here are her results.

Pre-4MAT

N = 73 questions

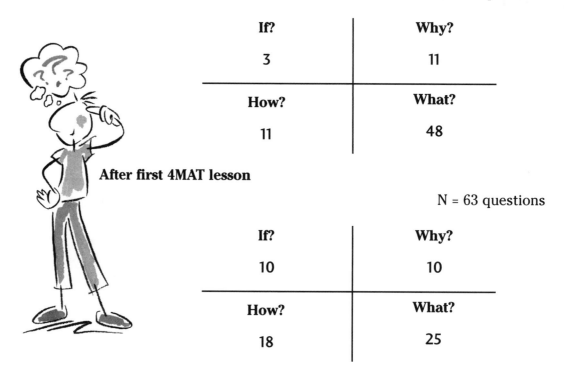

If?	Why?
3	11
How?	**What?**
11	48

After first 4MAT lesson

N = 63 questions

If?	Why?
10	10
How?	**What?**
18	25

After second 4MAT lesson

N = 61 questions

If?	Why?
14	13
How?	**What?**
12	22

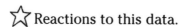 Reactions to this data.

Senior High School Learning Styles

Monroe, 1992

N = 74 in a private non-denominational school

(Both Type Two and Type Three learners had higher scores on the natural science section of the ACT than the Type Fours)

The researcher concluded that the secondary science curriculum would assist more students if it became more holistic in the presentation of concepts. The researcher recommended that both deductive and inductive information processing be added to instructional strategies. This means examining the possible future of the science being studied in addition to understanding its application in the present.

☆ What do you think about this researcher's conclusion and solution?

Type Fours	Type Ones
29	6
39%	8%
Type Threes	**Type Twos**
27	12
37%	16%

Hispanic Adults, Fort Worth, Texas

Missena, 1997

Males N = 53

Type Fours	Type Ones
5	19
9%	36%
Type Threes	**Type Twos**
18	11
34%	21%

Females N = 66

Type Fours	Type Ones
2	46
3%	70%
Type Threes	**Type Twos**
10	8
15%	12%

☆ How might you structure your instruction if these were your students? What would be most comfortable for them, most uncomfortable?

Research on Increases in Drop-Out Rates*

Linda Darling-Hammond, February, 2003

Stanford University

State of Massachusetts

300% increase in drop-outs between 1997-1998 and 1999-2000

Most of them African-American and Latino

Fewer drop-outs returning to school

Meanwhile the steepest positive increases in test scores are occurring in the same schools that have the highest retention and drop-out rates.

Similar trends in Texas with high increases in drop out rates in middle school and high school in the same schools where scores on standardized tests are going up sharply.

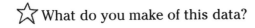 What do you make of this data?

---

*Standards and Assessments: Where We Are and What We Need
www.tcrecord.org (Linda Darling-Hammond, 2003)

Successful Trainer of Trainers Program Research

Griffin, 1997

University of Wisconsin, Madison

The following are the characteristics of a successful Trainer of Trainers Program

> Shared responsibility on the part of the school management team, the consulting agency (in this case study it was the staff) and the participants is absolutely essential.

Four other critical levers for success:

> The selection of suitable participants in a receptive and primed setting.

> The excellence of the training itself in terms of new roles for the participants, trainers, coaches, team lesson writers.

> The formation of learning teams.

> The inclusion of evaluation of the implementation.

☆ Are these things in place in your district?
  Which need more improvement?

Chapter Ten: Another Look at the Theory and the Research

Bibliography

Aitken, K. J. and C. Trevarthen. *Self-Other Organization in Human Psychological Development.* Development and Psychopathology, 9, 1997.

Abraham, Ralph H. and Christopher D. Shaw. Dynamics—The Geometry of Behavior, Part I: Periodic Behavior. *The Visual Mathematics Library.* Santa Cruz, CA: Aerial, 1984.

Baker, Eva L., Marie Freeman and Serena Clayton. Cognitive Assessment of Subject Matter: Understanding the Marriage of Psychological Theory and Educational Policy in Achievement Testing. CSE Technical Report #317. *UCLA Center for Research on Evaluation, Standards, and Student Testing,* 1990.

Benson, D. Frank and Eran Zaidel, Editors. *The Dual Brain: Hemispheric Specialization in Humans.* New York: The Guilford Press, 1985.

Benson, D. Frank. *The Neurology of Thinking.* New York: Oxford University Press, 1994.

Bogen, Joseph. Mental Duality in the Intact Brain. *Bulletin of Clinical Neurosciences,* Vol. 51, 1986.

Bohm, David. *Wholeness and the Implicate Order.* London, UK: Routledge, 1996.

Bradshaw, John and Norman Nettleton. *Human Cerebral Asymmetry.* Englewood Cliffs, NJ: Prentice-Hall, 1983.

Bransford, John. *How People Learn: Brain, Mind, Experience, and School.* Washington, DC: National Academy Press, 1999.

Bruner, Jerome. *On Knowing: Essays for the Left Hand.* Cambridge, MA: Harvard Univ. Press, 1962, 1979.

Bruner, Jerome. *Toward a Theory of Instruction.* Cambridge, MA: Harvard Univ. Press, 1966.

Carey, Ken. *The Third Millenium: Living in the Post-historic World.* San Francisco: Harper, 1996.

Carroll, Lewis. *The Complete Illustrated Works.* New York: Random House, 1995.

Cook-Greuter, Susanne, R. *Comprehensive Language Awareness: A Definition of the phenomenon and a review of its treatment in the post-formal adult development literature.* Harvard University Graduate School of Education thesis, 1995.

Damasio, Antonio. *The Feeling of What Happens: Body and Emotion in the Making of Consciousness.* New York: Harcourt Brace, 1999.

Defanti, Thomas, Maxine Brown and Bruce McCormick. "Visualization: Expanding Scientific and Engineering Research Opportunities", *Computer*, Vol. 22, No. 8, 1989.

Dewey, John. *John Dewey: The Later Works, 1925-1953.* Carbondale: Southern University Press, 1986. Original work published in 1933. Jo Ann Boydston, editor.

Dewey, John. *Experience and Education.* New York: MacMillan, 1938.

Diamond, Marian Cleeves. *Enriching Heredity: The Impact of the Environment on the Anatomy of the Brain.* New York: The Free Press, 1988.

Dillard, Annie. *Pilgrim at Tinker Creek.* Cutchogue, NY: Buccaneer Books, 1974.

Dreyfus, Stuart and Hubert. *Mind Over Machine: The Power of Human Intuition and Expertise in the Era of the Computer.* New York: MacMillan, 1985.

Freire, Paulo. *Pedagogy of the Oppressed.* New York: Continuum, 1970.

Frost, Robert. *The Figure a Poem Makes. Complete Poems.* London: Jonathan Cape, 1951.

Gardner, Howard. *Frames of Mind: The Theory of Multiple Intelligences.* New York: Basic Books, 1993.

Gardner, Howard. *Intelligence Reframed.* New York: Basic Books, 1999.

Gazzaniga, Michael S. *Nature's Mind: The Biological Roots of Thinking, Emotions, Sexuality, Language, and Intelligence.* New York: Basic Books, 1992.

Gelb, Michael. *How to Think Like Leonardo Da Vinci.* New York: Dell Books, 1998.

Gleick, James. *Chaos: Making a New Science.* New York: Penguin Books, 1987.

Goleman, Daniel. *Emotional Intelligence.* New York: Bantam Books, 1995.

Goodlad, John. *A Place Called School: Prospects for the Future.* New York: McGraw-Hill, 1984.

Gopnik, Alison, Andrew N. Meltzoff, and Patrician K. Kuhl. *The Scientist in the Crib: Minds, Brains, and How Children Learn.* New York: William Morrow, 1999.

Gould, Stephen Jay. *The Mismeasure of Man.* New York: W. W. Norton, 1981, 1996.

Graham, Jorie. *The Errancy: Poems.* Hopewell, NJ: The Ecco Press, 1997.

Greene, Maxine. "Texts and Margins," Arts as Education, M.R Goldberg and A. Phillips, Eds. Cambridge, MA: *Harvard Educational Review.* Reprint Series, number 24, 1992.

Greenspan, Stanley I. with Beryl Lieff Benderly. *The Growth of the Mind and the Endangered Origins of Intelligence.* Reading, MA: Perseus Books, 1997.

Hayes-Jacob, Heidi. *Interdisciplinary Curriculum: Design and Implementation.* Alexandria, VA: Association for Curriculum Development, 1989.

Healy, Jane. *Your Child's Growing Mind.* New York: Doubleday, 1994.

James, William. *The Will to Believe.* New York: Dover Publications, 1956.

Jung, Carl. *Psychological Types.* Princeton, NJ: Princeton University Press, 1976, original, 1923.

Kallick, Bena and Arthur Costa. "Through the Lens of a Critical Friend." *Educational Leadership.* Alexandria, VA: Association for Curriculum Development, February, 1991.

Kegan, Robert. *The Evolving Self: Problems and Process in Human Development.* Cambridge, MA: Harvard University Press, 1982.

Kolb, David A. *Experiential Learning: Experience as the Source of Learning and Development.* Englewood Cliffs, NJ: Prentice-Hall, 1983.

LeDoux, Joseph. *The Emotional Brain: the Mysterious Underpinnings of Emotional Life.* New York: Simon and Schuster, 1996.

Lewin, Kurt. *Field Theory in Social Sciences.* New York: Harper and Row, 1951.

Luria, Aleksandr. *Higher Cortical Functions in Man.* 2nd Edition. New York: Basic Books, 1980.

McCarthy, Bernice. *About Learning.* Wauconda, IL: About Learning, Inc., 1996.

McCarthy, Bernice and Susan Morris. *4MAT in Action: Lesson Units for All Grades, 4th Edition.* Wauconda, IL: About Learning, Inc., 1999.

McCarthy, Bernice. *About Teaching: 4MAT in The Classroom.* Wauconda, IL: About Learning, Inc., 2000.

McCarthy, Bernice. *About Teaching Companion.* Wauconda, IL: About Learning, Inc., 2003.

McCarthy, Dennis. *4MATION Software.* Wauconda, IL: About Learning, Inc., 1994, 1999, 2000.

McGinn, Colin. *The Mysterious Flame: Conscious Minds in a Material World.* New York: Basic Books, 1999.

(McREL)Mid-Continent Regional Educational Laboratory. (bound booklet #61) Aurora, CO. info@mcrel.org

Musick, Mark. *Setting Education Standards High Enough.* Atlanta, GA: Southern Regional Education Board, 1996.

Noddings, Nel and Paul J. Shore. *Awakening the Inner Eye: Intuition in Education.* New York: Columbia Teachers College Press, 1984.

Oliver, Mary. *Rules for the Dance.* Boston, MA: Houghton-Mifflin, 1998.

Ornstein, Robert. *The Right Mind: Making Sense of the Hemispheres.* New York: Harcourt Brace, 1997.

Perrone, Vito. "Toward More Powerful Assessment." *Educational Leadership. In Expanding Student Assessment.* Alexandria, VA: Association for Curriculum Development, 1991.

Piaget, Jean. *Child's Perception of the World.* New York: Basic Books, 1929, Reprint, 1990.

Popham, W. James. *Classroom Assessment: What Teachers Need to Know. 2nd Edition.* Boston, MA: Allyn and Bacon, 1999.

Ramachandran, V.S. and Sandra Blakeslee. *Phantoms in the Brain: Probing the Mysteries of the Human Mind.* New York: William Morrow, 1998.

Resnick, Lauren. *Education and Learning to Think.* Washington, D.C.: National Research Council, 1987.

Restak, Richard. *The Brain Has a Mind of Its Own: Insights From a Practicing Neurologist.* New York: Harmony Books, 1991.

Restak, Richard. *The Modular Brain.* New York: Simon and Schuster, 1994.

Rutherford, F. James and Andrew Ahlgren. *Science for All Americans.* New York: Oxford University Press, 1990.

Sanders, Judy and Don. *Teaching Creativity Through Metaphor.* New York: Longman, Inc, 1984.

Schacter, Daniel. *Searching for Memory: The Brain, The Mind, and The Past.* New York: Basic Books, 1996.

Senge, Peter M., Art Kliener, Charlotte Roberts, Richard B. Ross, and Bryan J. Smith. *The Fifth Discipline Field Book: Strategies and Tools for Building a Learning Organization.* New York: Doubleday, 1994.

Shlain, Leonard. *The Alphabet Versus the Goddess: The Conflict Between Word and Image.* New York: Viking, 1998.

Siegel, Daniel. *The Developing Mind: Toward a Neurobiology of Interpersonal Experience.* New York: The Guilford Press, 1999.

Storr, Anthony. *Music and the Mind.* New York: The Free Press, 1992.

Tenhouten, Warren D. *Cerebral-Lateralization Theory and the Sociology of Knowledge in The Dual Brain.* D. Frank Benson and Eran Zaidel editors. New York: The Guilford Press, 1985.

Tucker, Marc and Judy Codding. *Standards for Our Schools: How to Set Them, Measure Them, and Reach Them.* San Francisco: Jossey-Bass, 1998.

Vygotsky, L.S. *Mind in Society: The Development of Higher Psychological Processes.* Cambridge, MA: Harvard University Press, 1978.

West, Thomas G. *In the Mind's Eye: Visual Thinkers, Gifted People with Learning Difficulties, Computer Images, and the Ironies of Creativity.* Buffalo, NY: Prometheus Books, 1991.

Whyte, David. *The Heart Aroused; Poetry and the Preservation of the Soul in Corporate America.* New York: Doubleday, 1996.

Wiggins, Grant P. *Assessing Student Performance: Exploring the Purpose and Limits of Testing.* San Francisco, CA: Jossey-Bass, 1993.